75 Easy Chemistry Demonstrations

Thomas Kardos

illustrated by
Nicholas Soloway

J. WESTON
WALCH
PUBLISHER

PORTLAND, MAINE

Dedication

This book is dedicated to my darling wife, Pearl, who throughout this project assisted me with great patience. As a nonscience educator, she helped me develop this book into an easy-to-use and comprehensible resource.

1   2   3   4   5   6   7   8   9   10

ISBN 0-8251-2805-6

Copyright © 1996
J. Weston Walch, Publisher
P. O. Box 658 • Portland, Maine 04104-0658

Printed in the United States of America

Contents

Preface

As a middle school teacher, many times I found myself wishing for a quick and easy demonstration to illustrate a word, a concept, or a principle in science. Also I often wanted a brief explanation to conveniently review basics and additional information without going to many texts.

This book is a collection of many classroom demonstrations. Explanation is provided so that you can quickly review key concepts. Basic science ideas are hard to present on a concrete level; this book fills that specific need. Some of the demonstrations can be repeated at home and also can be adapted by you as student laboratory activities.

The actual teacher demonstration is something full of joy and expectation, like a thriller with an unexpected twist ending. Keep it that way and enjoy it! Try everything beforehand.

We need to support each other and leave footprints in the sands of time. Teaching is a living art. Happy journey! Happy sciencing!

—Thomas Kardos

MY PHILOSOPHY OF EDUCATION

My philosophy of education involves many themes:

1. Students must feel like participants in the joy of sciencing.

2. Students need many hands-on experiences. Invite them to experiment at home. This invitation must be limited by the availability of equipment and the relative safety of the activity. Experiments can be done with much informal equipment such as recycled jars, soda cans, and bottles. Inexpensive plastic measuring cups can replace graduated cylinders.

3. Students need to form in their own minds a concept of what science is. Do not encourage rote memorization. Science is a series of stories that need the participant's intervention. Let your students jump in and get involved in these stories.

4. Teachers do not have to answer all student questions. It is wonderful to let your students know that you are a limited resource. Let students go out and find some difficult answers. Maybe there are none. Nobody on this planet has all the answers. It is important that you teach your students the concept that humans have limits, but these can change. Let students know that through networking (cooperative effort) they, too, can find some of the harder answers.

5. People are concrete operators. Their learning starts with real objects and lots of manipulations and eventually ends in abstract reasoning and concept formation. This is why people draw sketches for you, to explain their ideas. Read summaries or explanations of Piaget's learning theory; it will change your teaching style for life.

6. Be open to change! Be prepared to change as you progress in teaching. The world around us changes and so must our teaching style.

7. Finally, realize that you cannot do it all. Your many science students become your followers. You will start a science revolution! This is your real opportunity!

Suggestions for Teachers

1. A • (bullet) denotes a demonstration. Several headings have multiple demonstrations.

2. MATERIALS: Provides an accurate list of materials needed. You can make substitutions and changes, as you find appropriate.

3. Since many demonstrations are small and are not clearly visible from the back of the room, you will need to take this into account as part of your classroom management technique. Students need to see the entire procedure, step by step.

4. Some demonstrations require that students make observations over a short period of time. It is important that students observe the changes in progress. One choice is to videotape the event and replay it several times.

5. Some demonstrations can be enhanced by bottom illumination: Place the demonstration on the overhead projector and lower the mirror so that no image is projected overhead.

6. Encourage students to repeat certain carefully selected demonstrations in class or at home.

7. Key words are included in the Index for easier access to the demonstrations.

8. I use a 30-cup coffeepot to heat water for student experiments and to perform many demonstrations in lieu of an electric hot plate, pans, and more cumbersome equipment.

9. I may use temperature Fahrenheit in some places, since the majority of younger students relate to it better.

10. Just a few demonstrations may appear difficult to set up, for they have many parts. Be patient, follow the listing's steps, and you will really succeed with them.

EQUIPMENT

- Sometimes, though rarely, I will call for equipment that you may not have. An increasing growth in technology tends to complicate matters. Skip these few demonstrations or borrow the equipment from your local high school teacher. Review with him or her the proper and safe use of it. These special demonstrations will add immensely to your power as an effective educator and will enhance your professionalism.

- Try all demonstrations in advance, to smooth your show. If something fails, enjoy it and teach with it. Many great science discoveries had to be done over many times before their first success. Dr. Land had to do more than 11,000 experiments to develop the instant color photograph. Most people would have quit long before that.

- One of my favorite techniques is to use a camcorder and show the demonstration on a large monitor.

SAFETY PROCEDURES

- Follow all local, state, and federal safety procedures: Protect your students and yourself from harm.

- Attend safety classes to be up-to-date on the latest in classroom safety procedures. Much new legislation has been adopted in the recent past.

- Have evacuation plans clearly posted, planned, and actually tested.

- Have an ABC-rated fire extinguisher on hand at all times. Use a Halon™ gas extinguisher for electronic equipment.

- Learn how to use a fire extinguisher properly.

- Label all containers and use original containers.

- Wear required safety equipment when handling hazardous materials, such as laboratory acids or anything stronger than ordinary vinegar.

- Practice your demonstration if it is totally new to you. A few demonstrations do require some prior practice.

- Conduct demonstrations at a distance so that no one is harmed, should anything go wrong.

- Have students wash their hands whenever they come into contact with anything that may be remotely harmful to them, even if years later, like lead.

- Neutralize all acids and bases prior to disposal.

- Dispose of demonstration materials in a safe way. Obtain your district's guidelines on this matter.

DISCLAIMER

The safety rules are provided only as a guide. They are neither complete nor totally inclusive. The publisher and the author do not assume any responsibility for actions or consequences in following instructions provided in this demonstration book.

1. MATTER, MASS, AND WEIGHT

Mass is the property of being a material object. Solids, liquids, and gases are made up of molecules, the building blocks of all matter in the universe. If one combines mass with the pull of gravity, a force, then one has weight. Scales measure the pull of gravity on mass. Mass does not change on earth, although weight may. An object at different latitudes or heights may show a different weight, for the force of earth's gravity will vary. An orange has the same mass at sea level, on the top of Mount Everest, or in orbit. On earth, the orange has a certain weight at sea level, and less weight on top of a mountain. In orbit, the orange has no weight, for there is no force of gravity. That explains how the shuttle crew can pick up a large satellite in space.

MATERIALS: two glasses or beakers, enough water to fill one container

- **Matter takes up space and has mass.** Take two glasses and fill one with water. Have students lift both glasses. Have them comment on the difference in glass masses. The one that is full of water has more mass and feels heavier. If you step on a scale, the scale shows an increase in weight. This shows that humans are made of matter and have mass.

2. MATTER TAKES UP SPACE (VOLUME)

MATERIALS: cup or glass, flat pan, water, small rock or other object, balloon

- Place a cup or a glass in a flat pan and fill the glass to the brim with water. Place an eraser, rock, or other small object in the glass. The water will overflow. The object occupies space and displaces its own volume of water.

- Blow air into a balloon and observe how it appears to grow. Even though air is invisible, it occupies space and is matter.

Rock in Water

3. MATTER CAN BE A SOLID

Matter can be in solid form. Material objects are solid, have volume (take up a certain amount of space), and have a specific shape.

- Have students touch any object around them, such as a pencil, a table, or a book.

- Push a book with a pencil or finger. Notice that two objects cannot occupy the same space at the same time. The results of a car crash prove this basic law of matter.

4. MATTER CAN BE A LIQUID

Matter can be a liquid. In liquid form, molecules slide over one another. Liquids have a definite volume but take the shape of the container.

MATERIALS: glass or beaker, balloon, water

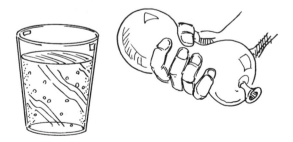

- Fill a glass with water. Fill a balloon with water and tie a knot at the end. Squeeze the balloon. Notice how the water takes the shape of its container.

5. MATTER CAN BE A GAS

Matter can be a gas. Gases take the shape of their container and have no definite volume.

MATERIALS: balloon, glass, piece of tissue, fish tank, water

- Blow air into a balloon. The balloon size will increase. Air does occupy space, as all matter does. Bend and twist the balloon. Notice how the gas inside it takes the distorted shape of the balloon.

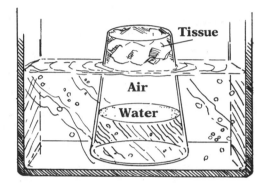

- Pour some water into the fish tank. Place a piece of tissue inside the bottom of a glass. Invert the glass and place it in the fish tank. Lift the glass from the tank and observe that the tissue is dry. Air displaced the water, and the tissue did not get wet.

6. GAS CAN BE COMPRESSED

Gases can be compressed. Molecules of gases are squeezed together during compression. The air inside bicycle and automobile tires is compressed. NASA compresses space shuttle fuel until it becomes liquid. In this manner, 600 gallons of gas occupy only the space of 1 gallon. To be compressed to a liquid, gases must also be cooled down. Propane for backyard barbecues is in liquid form. If it were in gas form, one would need many tanks full of gas to cook a steak.

MATERIALS: balloon

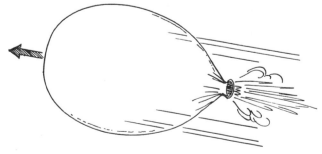

- Inflate a balloon as much as you can. You are compressing the air inside the balloon. Let the balloon go. It will fly away erratically. The pressurized air exits, and the balloon flies in the opposite direction.

7. PHYSICAL CHANGE

A **physical change** occurs when a material changes its size or shape but still remains the same material.

MATERIALS: piece of paper, rubber band, toothpick

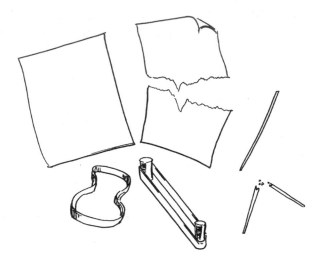

- Take a piece of paper and tear it. It is still paper. Take a rubber band and stretch it. It is still rubber. Take a toothpick and break it. It is still wood.

8. CHEMICAL CHANGE

A **chemical change** (**reaction**) occurs when a new substance is produced, unlike the original ones (reactants). It will have new physical and chemical properties. Chemical changes are associated with:

1. New substance (different chemical and physical properties)

2. Change in color

3. Giving off gases

4. Change in shape

5. Giving off heat energy (**exothermic**)

6. Needing heat energy (**endothermic**)

All of these need not be visible for a chemical reaction to take place.

MATERIALS: piece of paper, matches, beaker, baking soda, water, vinegar, pan, stirrer

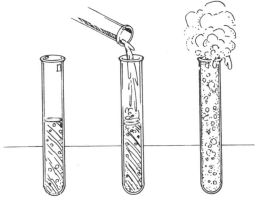

- Light a match and use it to burn a small piece of paper. The fire causes a chemical change (change in color, gases, change in shape, exothermic).

- In a beaker, mix some baking soda with water. Next, pour some vinegar into the baking soda solution to show a rapid chemical change.

9. MIXTURES

When two or more elements and compounds are mixed together and form *no new materials,* this is a **mixture**. A mixture can be separated again with some effort. A mixture is a physical change.

MATERIALS: salt, few beans, transparent sheet of acetate, overhead projector

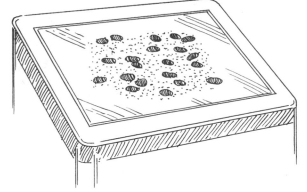

- Place the sheet of acetate on your overhead projector. Sprinkle some salt and mix some beans with it. Remove the beans. This illustrates how a mixture is made and its elements are separated.

10. SEPARATING A MIXTURE OF SALT AND WATER

Mixtures involving liquids are **solutions**. Chemists separate dissolved substances (**solute**) from water (**solvent**) by **evaporation**, a physical change. In a solution, the solvent is the material that does the dissolving.

MATERIALS: salt, beaker, hot plate, water, plastic spoon

- Prepare a mixture of salt and water by stirring salt into a beaker about half-full of water. Place the beaker on the hot plate and let all the water boil away (evaporate). Inside the hot beaker, you will find the solute, salt that was earlier in solution.

11. SEPARATING SUSPENDED AND DISSOLVED SOLIDS FROM WATER

In addition to dissolved minerals, water may contain floating or suspended solids. The floating and suspended particles are solids that do not dissolve in the liquid. These particles can be separated from water by filtering the liquid through an extra-fine porous paper membrane.

MATERIALS: water, filter paper, funnel, sand, two beakers, salt or baking soda, hot plate

- Mix water with salt or baking soda until some precipitates on the bottom. Add some sand. Fold a filter paper in half and half again and place it inside a funnel. Place the funnel into the receiving beaker and pour the liquid with suspended solids into the funnel. The particles of sand are too large to pass through the very fine pores of the filter and will remain on the filter paper. To remove the dissolved solids, evaporate the water from the filtered liquid. Both of these processes are physical changes.

12. COMPOUNDS

When two or more elements or compounds are combined to create a new substance, a compound is formed. New substances do not have the properties of the materials that make them up. Compounds are the result of chemical changes.

MATERIALS: test tube, forceps, sulfur, iron filings, magnet, Bunsen burner, several small dishes, pancake mix, small frying pan, cooking oil, hot plate, egg, saucepan, beaker, hot sulfuric acid, granulated sugar, water, glass stirrer rod, beaker-sized forceps, baking soda

- Place some powdered sulfur in a dish. Place some iron filings in a separate dish. Show your students how a magnet attracts the filings. Mix the iron filings with the sulfur and show how the magnet can be used to separate the mixture. Fill half the test tube with the sulfur-iron mixture. Use the Bunsen burner to heat the mixture until it begins to glow. Remove from the heat. Pour the material into a dish. Notice that its appearance is unlike either of the original substances. Try to use the magnet to separate the iron or to lift the mass. It will not work, for the new compound is nonmagnetic. This is an **endothermic** chemical reaction.

- Combine some pancake mix with water. Show students that you have a mixture. Now bake a pancake or two and show how a chemical reaction has taken place. A new substance has been formed: Bubbles of gas have appeared; the color has changed; and gases have been given off (aroma throughout the classroom). Point out that creating the new compound required heat energy. This was also an endothermic reaction.

- Cook an egg until it becomes hard-boiled. The contents begin as a liquid, but after the application of heat, they become solid. This endothermic chemical reaction cannot be reversed.

> **CAUTION!** The following is best done outdoors. The caramel fumes are strong. Keep students at least 8 to 10 feet away. Wear goggles, gloves, an apron, and other appropriate safety equipment.

- Fill the beaker with granulated sugar about 2 to 3 centimeters deep. Add enough hot sulfuric acid to cover the sugar. The hot sulfuric acid is clear, like water. You will observe the sugar turning to yellow, brown, and black. The action may require several minutes. By using a glass stirrer, you may speed up the reaction rate. Stir the sugar and acid together; then promptly remove the stirrer. This chemical reaction is **exothermic**. Suddenly you will see a puff of smoke and the reaction will speed up. The sugar in the beaker will turn into a large, growing cylinder of carbon. The smell will suggest that the sugar has burned. It has done so chemically.

• Holding the beaker with forceps, let students touch the bottom of the hot beaker. Do not let them touch the piece of coal, which is soaked with hot sulfuric acid. The reason the coal lump is bigger than the original volume of sugar is that carbon dioxide is given off during the reaction. The carbon dioxide forms bubbles in the carbon mass, just as it does it when bread dough rises. Wash the carbon piece with a lot of water to cool it and to dilute the acid contents. Then neutralize it with a strong baking soda solution before disposal. Your students will enjoy this activity immensely. In one activity, you demonstrated a strong chemical reaction, spontaneous combustion (when the sugar gives off the puff of smoke), and all the classical components of a chemical change.

Sugar and Acid

13. SUBSTANCES CONTAIN MORE THAN ONE ELEMENT

Most matter around us is composed of more than one element. Matter can be a combination of several elements, an element and a molecule (a compound), or molecules combined with other molecules. A molecule by itself is a combination of two or more atoms, which may be different or the same. A diatomic element is one that travels in pairs, such as Br_2 (bromine), Cl_2 (chlorine), F_2 (fluorine), I_2 (iodine), H_2 (hydrogen), O_2 (oxygen), and N_2 (nitrogen). In this activity, you will separate two elements from each other—a chemical change.

MATERIALS: test tube, mercuric oxide, Bunsen burner, forceps, splint

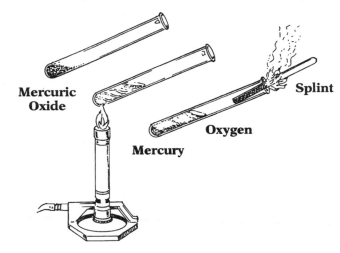

- Place a teaspoon of mercuric oxide in a test tube and heat it. After a while, the orange-colored powder will turn into a shiny, silvery liquid—mercury. Conduct a splint test for oxygen. Light a splint and blow out the fire. While the splint is still glowing, place it into the test tube. The splint will burst into a flame if there is any oxygen in the test tube. You have just separated mercury from oxygen. This is a classic experiment.

14. TWO GASES FORM A SOLID (AMMONIUM CHLORIDE)

MATERIALS: two small wads of cotton, two paper clips, dilute hydrochloric acid, ammonium hydroxide (ammonia), glass

- Bend both paper clips open. Hook a small wad of cotton on one end of each. Make a hook on the opposite ends of the clips, so that they can hang on the rim of the glass. Dip one cotton wad in dilute hydrochloric acid, the other one in ammonia. Hang the clips on the opposite edges of the glass. Inside the glass, you will notice a cloud of ammonium chloride and later a deposit of visible salt.

15. TWO LIQUIDS FORM A SOLID (NYLON)

In this demonstration, when you unite two colorless liquids in a glass container, they begin to form a solid as the liquids interact. The two solutions are immiscible, and you will observe their two distinct layers. Their interface, the joint border of both liquids, is the synthesis of a polymer, nylon 66. A polymer is a long molecule, made of many small molecules called monomers.

MATERIALS: two test tubes, paper clip, graduated 10-milliliter cylinder, adipoyl chloride/hexane solution, hexamethylenediamine/sodium hydroxide solution (*Source:* Flint Scientific Inc., P.O. Box 219, 131 Flynn Street, Batavia, IL 60510, (708) 879-6900, Catalog #H0032 and #A0185.)

> **CAUTION!** Hexamethylenediamine is a strong tissue irritant and is toxic if ingested. Adipoyl chloride/hexane solution is a flammable liquid and is toxic if ingested or inhaled. Use a face shield, chemical-resistant gloves, and a chemical-resistant apron. Observe prudent laboratory practices.

- Follow these steps in their exact order:

1. Add 7 milliliters of hexamethylenediamine/sodium hydroxide solution to a test tube.

2. Very slowly add 7 milliliters of adipoyl chloride/hexane solution to the side of the test tube. It will help if you hold this test tube at about 45°. *Do not stir or mix the solutions.* Note how a film forms where the two solutions intcrfacc.

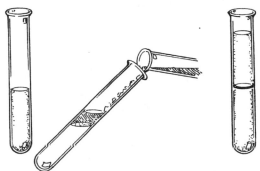

3. Bend a paper clip and pull the film from the beaker. As the nylon gets long, support it with another test tube in your other hand. Pull slowly until there is no nylon left.

4. Wash the nylon several times before you or students handle it.

5. Dispose of leftover chemicals in a safe manner as described on the bottles.

16. PREPARING OXYGEN FROM PEROXIDE

The standard over-the-counter 3% peroxide provides a safe way to produce oxygen. The formula for a molecule of peroxide is H_2O_2. Peroxide contains an extra oxygen atom as compared to a molecule of water (H_2O).

MATERIALS: rust (iron oxide), small bottle or test tube, peroxide, cookie sheet or pie tin (must be metal), splint, matches, hot plate, beaker, water

- Pour a small amount of iron oxide (rust) into a test tube or small bottle containing peroxide. Place this test tube into hot water and watch oxygen bubbles float up to the surface. To test for oxygen, use the splint test while the test tube is in the hot water.

- Pour the peroxide onto a cookie sheet and observe how it bubbles. It is generating oxygen.

17. ELECTROLYSIS OF WATER

In this demonstration, you will be separating water into its two parent gases: oxygen and hydrogen. The process of separating water into its constituent gases is **electrolysis**. If you have a Hoffman apparatus, you do not need to build the following.

MATERIALS: shallow tumbler, water, glass, two test tubes, insulated copper wire, two battery clips, eight D-size batteries with holders or a 12 V DC power supply (car battery or toy train transformer), switch, splint, matches, sodium sulfate, pliers or tongs, two stainless steel bolts or large screws

Sodium sulfate (a safer chemical) replaces hydrochloric acid, normally recommended for this activity.

- Follow these steps:

1. Bare about 2 inches of an 18-inch copper wire and wrap it tightly around a stainless steel screw or bolt. Repeat for the other bolt.

2. As shown in the diagram, run one wire to the positive end of all your batteries in series (or DC power supply), and the other wire to the switch that connects to the negative end of the batteries (or DC power supply). Connections to batteries are simpler if you have battery holders; otherwise solder the wires to the batteries.

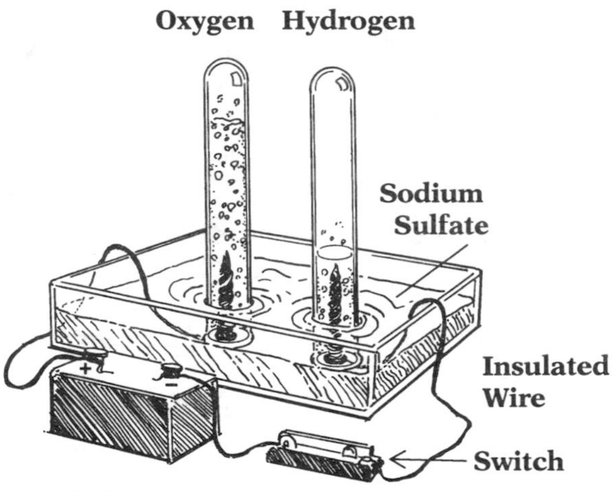

Oxygen   Hydrogen

Sodium Sulfate

Insulated Wire

Switch

3. Fill the tumbler with a solution of sodium sulfate. Mix as much sodium sulfate as one glass of water will dissolve.

4. Fill a test tube with the sodium sulfate solution, and hold it tightly stoppered with your thumb. Invert the test tube and place it in the tumbler. Repeat for the other one.

5. Place one stainless steel screw into the test tube. Repeat for the other one.

6. Close the switch. Observe that gas bubbles more rapidly in the test tube connected to the negative end of the power supply than in the other one. Inside the test tube, hydrogen makes a column of gas twice as high as the one on the positive end, containing oxygen.

7. Test for oxygen and hydrogen. Do a splint test for oxygen. To test for hydrogen, perform a modified splint test: Light the splint and leave it lit. When you place the flame near the mouth of the test tube, you will hear a small "pop" sound, typical of hydrogen explosions.

18. SEPARATING THE ELEMENTS IN SALT

The elements that make up salt are sodium and chlorine. Sodium is a highly reactive metal, while chlorine is a poisonous greenish gas. The formula for salt is NaCl (sodium chloride). This compound can be separated through the process of electrolysis. Chlorine gas will form over the positive carbon rod, while the sodium will be dissolved in the water to form a weak solution of sodium hydroxide (household lye).

MATERIALS: two dead D-size batteries, two battery clips, insulated copper wire, tumbler, water, 6 V DC power supply (or four D-size batteries or toy train transformer), soldering iron, switch, salt, water, phenolphthalein

- Follow these steps:

1. Take apart the two dead batteries to recover their center carbon rods.

2. Using tongs or pliers, hold the carbon rods over the open fire of a kitchen stove to remove any residual wax. Keep the rods on the fire until they turn a slight red; then allow them to cool.

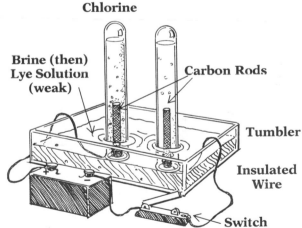

3. Attach a battery clip to each carbon rod. Attach one copper wire to this clip.

4. Attach one end of a wire to the positive end of the batteries. Attach the other wire to the switch.

5. Mix a salt solution (brine) and fill half of the tumbler.

6. Fill one test tube with brine, and insert the carbon rod into it. Holding your thumb over the mouth of the test tube, invert it and place it in the brine. Repeat for the other test tube.

7. Close the switch.

8. Chlorine will form over the positive electrode. Since the amount is minute, it will represent no danger. For comparison, test plain water and brine with phenolphthalein; no color change will be visible. Test the water containing sodium hydroxide (formerly only brine) with phenolphthalein. Phenolphthalein will turn pink. Sodium hydroxide is a base.

19. PROPERTIES OF METALS AND NONMETALS

Here is a summary of key properties of metals and nonmetals:

PROPERTIES	NONMETALS	METALS
State	Solid, liquid, or gas. Bromine is only liquid.	Solids. Mercury is liquid.
Color	Nonshiny, except iodine	Shiny, bright, many colors
Conducts heat	Poor conductors	Good conductors
Conducts electricity	Poor conductors, except graphite	Good conductors
Ductility	Brittle	Ductile
Malleability	Brittle	Malleable
Boiling point	Generally low	Generally high
Melting point	Generally low	Generally high

MATERIALS: piece of metal coat hanger (or other metal), piece of wood or dowel (both about 6 to 10 inches long), beaker with water, Bunsen burner

- Heat the ends of both a wood stick and a piece of metal. Notice how the metal hanger transmits the heat. If the wood catches on fire, dip it in the beaker of water.

20. METALS CONDUCT HEAT

Metals conduct heat. The molecules of metal transmit heat energy by passing their energy to their neighbors.

MATERIALS: dominoes, 12- to 18-inch metal rod (wire coat hanger or copper wire), handle or small wooden block, several tacks, wax, Bunsen burner

- Line up a row of dominoes and show your students how once you push over the first one, they all fall. Explain that metals transmit heat in the same manner.

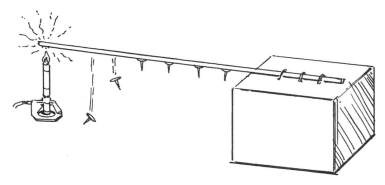

- Fasten the metal rod to the block or handle. Attach tacks along the length of the rod with wax. Heat the free end of the rod with a Bunsen burner and watch the tacks gradually drop off as the heat is transmitted. So that the process will be a gradual one, do not bring the burner too close to the rod.

21. NONMETALS DO NOT CONDUCT HEAT

Nonmetals are poor conductors of heat. If enough heat is applied, they reach their kindling temperature and burn, oxidizing rapidly. In the second part of this demonstration, the paper cup will not burn, because the water will act as a coolant. The water will absorb the heat energy, and the paper will not reach its kindling temperature.

MATERIALS: Bunsen burner, paper cup (that does not have edges pointing down), saucepan, water, thermometer, forceps

- Holding the cup with the forceps, place it in the flames and show how readily it will burn. Do it near a sink or a pan of water, so that you can quickly extinguish the fire.

- Fill the cup nearly to the top with water. Take the temperature of the water. Using the forceps, hold the cup over the flame until the water begins to boil. Recheck its temperature. Point out to your students that the tip of the flame is hotter than 3000°F or 1650°C.

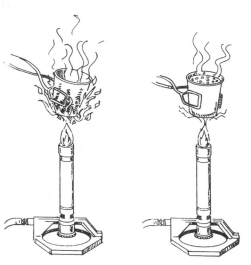

22. METALS CONDUCT ELECTRICITY

Metals are good conductors of electricity. Nonmetals are usually poor conductors of electricity. Certain nonmetals like quartz and silicone conduct electricity under certain conditions; therefore they are semiconductors. Mercury, the only metal that is liquid at room temperature, is used in household and industrial switches to make silent electrical connections.

MATERIALS: bulb base, 1.5 V flashlight bulb, 1.5 V battery, rubber band, battery holder, insulated fine wire, coin, piece of silverware, other metal objects to be tested

- Connect the simple circuit as shown in the illustration. Unless you have a battery holder, fasten the wires to the battery either with a rubber band or with a drop or two of solder. Cut one of the wires and strip off the insulation at the cut point. Touch both wires to the coin. The bulb will light up, showing the metal's conductivity of electricity. Repeat this test, using silverware and other metal objects.

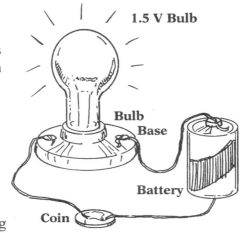

23. EXCEPTIONS TO NONCONDUCTIVITY OF NONMETALS

Nonmetals do not conduct electricity unless they are semiconductors. Typically these are substances such as quartz or silicone, used in transistors, diodes, integrated circuits, and the like. This group of nonmetals will conduct electric current only under some conditions. Certain plastics have a shiny, metallic appearance. They may conduct electricity, because they had metal added to their surfaces through a vacuum deposit process. Certain other nonmetalliferous plastics may also conduct electricity. This last group has been designed to be electroconductive.

MATERIALS: bulb base, 1.5 V flashlight bulb, 1.5 V battery, rubber band, battery holder, insulated fine wire, coin, block of wood, other nonmetal objects to be tested

- Connect the simple circuit as shown in the illustration. Unless you have a battery holder, fasten the wires to the battery either with a rubber band or with a drop of solder. Cut one of the wires and strip off the insulation at the cut point. Touch both wires to the coin. The bulb will light up, showing the metal's conductivity of electricity. This first test shows that your setup works. Now, repeat the test, using nonmetal objects, such as wood, paper, glass, plastics.

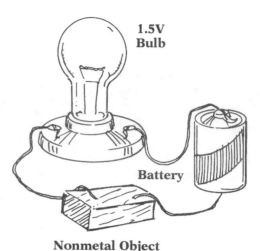

24. METALS HAVE LUSTER

Metals have a shine, or **luster**. If a metal does not shine, scratch it with a nail to show its real luster.

MATERIALS: nonmetallic objects, metal objects—tinfoil, coins, copper wire, lead sinker, paper clips

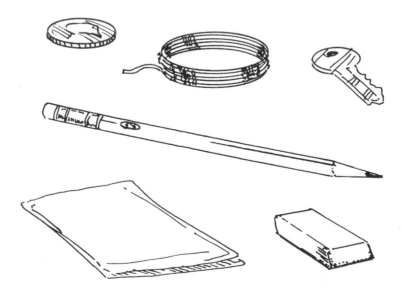

- Show your students how all metals have the property of luster, or shine. They reflect light. Compare the metals with nonmetals. Most nonmetals do not have luster.

25. NONMETALS ARE BRITTLE AND NOT MALLEABLE

Some elements are nonmetals. Nonmetals are poor conductors of electricity and heat and are brittle. If you hit a piece of coal or sulfur with a hammer, it will break into small pieces. Nonmetals can be gases, liquids, or solids. To be malleable means that a substance can be hammered into sheets. Nonmetals are not malleable.

MATERIALS: hammer, piece of coal, piece of sulfur, sugar cube

- Hit the coal and the sulfur with the hammer. They will shatter into many small pieces. Repeat with the sugar cube.

26. DIFFERENT METALS AND NONMETALS CONDUCT HEAT DIFFERENTLY

Different metals conduct heat at different rates. Nonmetals are poor conductors of heat.

MATERIALS: wooden block with several identical rods of different metal and nonmetal materials (glass, iron, brass, copper, aluminum), Bunsen burner, wax, tacks

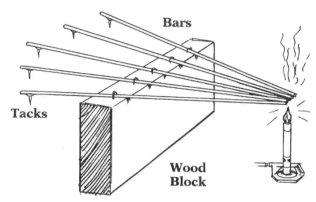

- Install the rods on the wooden block by fastening them at their middle. On one end, join all the rod ends close together. At the opposite end, attach a tack to each rod with some wax. Observe the order in which the tacks fall. This will demonstrate the varying speeds of heat transfer for different metal and nonmetal materials.

27. GLASS IS A POOR HEAT CONDUCTOR

Nonmetals are poor conductors of heat. Point out to your students that glass is a poor conductor of heat. This causes problems. If one pours hot liquids into a glass, the inner part of the glass heats up much more rapidly than the outside and expands. At this point the glass breaks. If the glass walls were thin, this problem would be minimized. Boron is added to Pyrex™ glass to decrease the amount of shrinkage and expansion, eliminating most of the thermal stress. Since nonmetals are poor conductors of heat, they are used as **insulators** to prevent the transfer of heat. Notice that most vacuum bottles have an inserted glass bottle.

MATERIALS: Bunsen burner, test tube, water

- Fill the test tube one-third full of water and hold it by the top. Tilt the test tube about 45°. Bring the test tube near the flame and boil the water. You will be able to hold the test tube without a problem because glass transmits heat poorly.

28. WHY METALS CORRODE

When a nail rusts, a penny loses its shine, a silver spoon becomes black, or an aluminum pot becomes dull, one observes signs of metal corrosion. This wearing away of the metal is a chemical change. Metals oxidize when exposed to oxygen in air, water, or soil. When iron oxidizes, it forms rust. When copper pipe or pennies oxidize, they form verdigris. When a metal oxidizes, it loses electrons to a nonmetal, oxygen. When silver oxidizes, it forms tarnish. Silver actually combines with sulfur, not oxygen. Sulfur gets into the air from burned fuels and from gases released by volcanoes. In corrosion, both the metal and the nonmetal become ions (electrically charged atoms). An example of oxidation:

Copper　　+　　Oxygen　　➡　　verdigris (copper oxide)

Cu　　　+　　O　　➡　　CuO

The copper loses two electrons; the oxygen gains two electrons. For metals, oxidation is the loss of electrons.

Cu°	−2 electrons ➡	Cu^{+2}
O°	+2 electrons ➡	O^{-2}
Basic Atoms		Ions

MATERIALS: silver spoon or silver coin, hard-boiled egg

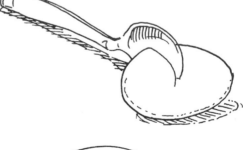

- Push only a part of a silver spoon into the egg white, after removing the shell. Remove the spoon after several minutes. Since the egg contains sulfur, there will be a black coating on part of the silver spoon. The tarnish can be removed with silver polish.

29. LIQUIDS ARE POOR CONDUCTORS OF HEAT

Nonmetals are poor conductors of heat. **Liquids** are also poor conductors of heat.

MATERIALS: small ice cube, test tube, Bunsen burner, water, coin or ball-point pen spring, forceps

- Fill the test tube three-quarters full of water. Add to it a small ice cube. Weigh the ice cube down with a coin, so that it does not float. You may use a ballpoint pen spring, paper clip, or other small object in place of the coin. Hold the test tube with forceps so that students can view the entire tube. Heat the upper part of the test tube, and water will boil away while most of the ice cube remains in place. The bottom will not heat up.

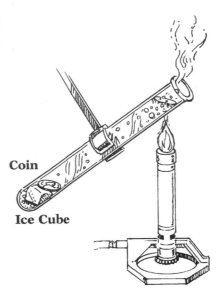

Coin

Ice Cube

30. CARBON DIOXIDE

MATERIALS: balloon, bicarbonate of soda (baking soda), small bottle, vinegar, funnel, water, tablespoon, glass, stirrer, test tube, limewater

- Fill a glass half-full of water and place in it two or three teaspoons of baking soda. Stir the liquid until most of the powder is dissolved. Fill the bottle with the liquid. Fill the balloon with about three tablespoons of vinegar. Gently place the balloon opening over the bottle top, being careful so that it hangs and no vinegar spills into the bottle. Lift the balloon and observe the fizzing and bubbling in the bottle, when the vinegar meets the solution of water and baking soda. The chemical reaction has produced **carbon dioxide**, which now appears to fill the balloon. If you shake the bottle a little, the reaction will appear to continue for a while longer. Pass the bottle and balloon around. Point out to students that the balloon falls down because carbon dioxide is heavier than air.

- Test the carbon dioxide gas by pouring some limewater into the balloon. Pour the limewater back into the test tube and observe. It will turn milky white. Another choice is to pour the limewater into a glass and to slowly bubble the gas from the balloon through the liquid.

31. CARBON DIOXIDE FIRE EXTINGUISHER

Carbon dioxide is a gas that is heavier than air. If you pour it from one container into another one, it will go down into the second container, displacing the air.

MATERIALS: glass jar, candle, matches, equipment from Demonstration 30, page 24

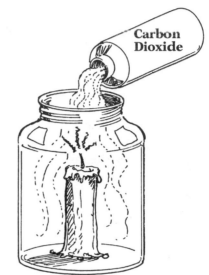

- Prepare carbon dioxide as described in Demonstration 30, Carbon Dioxide, page 24. Place a candle on the bottom of a jar, then light it. Gently allow the carbon dioxide to fill the jar. The flame will go out. Carbon dioxide displaces the air in the jar, and there is no oxygen left to support the candle's flame. Many fire extinguishers use carbon dioxide, although nowadays the gas halon is quickly replacing it.

- An alternative activity would be to fill a jar with the carbon dioxide from the balloon, and then gently pour the gas over the candle flame. This alternate way will demonstrate the weight of carbon dioxide.

32. ATOMS—ATOMIC CHARGES— RULE OF CHARGES

Information about atoms is highly theoretical, and all modeling can be done only with activities that parallel the ideas being described. **Atom** comes from a Greek word meaning *indivisible*. An atom is the smallest indivisible chunk of matter that has its own identity. If one goes further and breaks up the atom itself, then one has only charges. Atoms have a **nucleus** (center) and are surrounded by orbiting electrical charges. In the nucleus, there are positive charges (**protons**) and neutral charges (**neutrons**). Negative charges (**electrons**) spin around the nucleus. For every proton in the nucleus, there is one balancing electron in orbit. Therefore, on the whole, the atom is neutral: it is neither positive nor negative.

The Rule of Charges

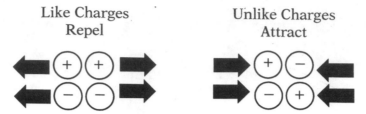

Like Charges
Repel

Unlike Charges
Attract

MATERIALS: two bar magnets, string

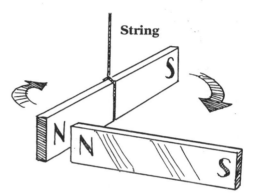

String

- Hang a small magnet by a string and allow it to come to rest. Bring another magnet near it and observe how one end of the magnet attracts the hanging magnet, while the other one repels it. Magnets use north and south instead of + and –.

33. MAKING AN ELECTROSCOPE

An **electroscope** is a very delicate instrument that detects the presence of electrons. It has been used to detect cosmic rays. If the electroscope leaves are charged with the same charges, the foil leaves repel and move apart.

MATERIALS: glass bottle, cork, large needle, length of #16 solid copper wire, thin aluminum foil, regular aluminum foil, two pins, plastic comb, nylon-wool cloth or piece of fur

Thin aluminum foil can be obtained by soaking chewing gum wrappers in alcohol to separate the paper from the foil, or from science supply houses.

- Follow these steps:

1. Bore a fine hole through the cork with the needle to allow the wire to go through the center.

2. Bend one end of the wire 90° to form the letter *L*. The bend should be approximately 1 inch. Fit it to be about 4 inches from the bottom of the bottle.

3. The copper wire should stick through the cork about 1 inch.

4. Cut the thin aluminum foil into rectangular leaves, each about $\frac{1}{2}$ inch wide by 3 inches long.

5. Use two pins to attach the leaves to the horizontal part of the copper wire.

6. Make a small ball out of the regular aluminum foil and attach it to the top of the copper wire, above the cork.

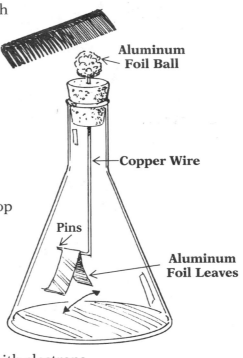

- Rub the comb briskly with a piece of nylon-wool cloth. Alternatively use a piece of fur. Bring the comb near the ball on top of the bottle and observe the leaves move apart. You have just charged both leaves with electrons.

34. SOLUTIONS: SOLIDS AND LIQUIDS

Solids that dissolve in liquids are **soluble**. Those that do not dissolve are **insoluble**. Liquids that mix with other liquids are **miscible**. Those that do not dissolve are **immiscible**.

MATERIALS: test tube rack, eight test tubes, water, teaspoon, salt, sugar, oil, vinegar, alcohol, iron filings, sulfur, kerosene

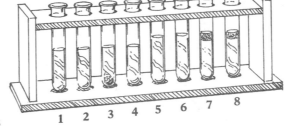

- Half-fill four test tubes with water. In test tubes 1–4, mix the water with about a teaspoon of each substance as indicated: sugar (1), salt (2), iron filings (3), and sulfur (4). Sugar and salt are soluble; iron filings and sulfur are not soluble. In test tubes 5–8, add two teaspoons of water. Next add two teaspoons of vinegar to test tube 5, two teaspoons of alcohol to 6, two teaspoons of oil to 7, and two teaspoons of kerosene to 8. Try to mix test tubes 5–8 with a stirrer. Vinegar and alcohol are miscible; oil and kerosene are immiscible with water.

35. SOLUTIONS AND SUSPENSIONS

A substance that dissolves other substances is a **solvent**. The substance that becomes dissolved is the **solute**. Solutions are mixtures. If they are uniform throughout, they are **homogeneous**. Milk is not a solution. It is a **suspension** of tiny butterfat particles that are suspended throughout the liquid, giving it its milky appearance. Solutions are clear and homogeneous. In a solution, the solvent breaks down the solute to a molecular size, and then they mix together. Suspension occurs when particles (groups of atoms, molecules, and ions) are larger than molecular sizes and do not dissolve.

MATERIALS: four identical flasks or glass jars, water, milk, salad oil, detergent, copper sulfate, sugar, starch, filter, filter funnel, tablespoon, microscope, slides

Sugar   Milk

Copper Sulfate   Starch

- Fill three flasks or jars three-quarters full of water. Dissolve sugar (two tablespoons) in one, copper sulfate (one tablespoon) in the next, and place one tablespoon of starch in the third bottle. Fill the fourth container with milk. Shake the sugar and copper sulfate flasks to dissolve the solids. Vigorously shake the flask containing the starch. Show the class how copper sulfate and sugar in solution are clear and homogeneous. The milk is not clear, and the starch is cloudy. The last two are suspensions, not solutions. Filter the copper sulfate and sugar to show that the liquid does not change; its molecular-size particles go through the filter. Filter the starch suspension and note the filtering out of starch grains.

- Show one drop of copper sulfate and one drop of starch suspension under the microscope. The copper sulfate will be clear regardless of magnification; it is a molecular-size solution. The starch solution will have visible starch grains.

36. OTHER SOLVENTS

Many substances that do not dissolve in water will dissolve in other solvents. Nail polish dissolves only in nail polish remover (acetone), iodine dissolves in alcohol, oil dissolves in solvents (lighter forms of hydrocarbons), oil-based paint dissolves in paint thinner, etc.

MATERIALS: lighter fluid, salad oil, two test tubes, water

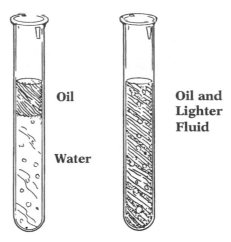

Oil

Water

Oil and Lighter Fluid

> **CAUTION!** Lighter fluid is a combustible fluid. It contains naphtha.

- Pour some oil into a test tube half-full of water. The two substances do not mix. Add oil to a test tube half-full of lighter fluid and shake it. The lighter fluid will dissolve the oil.

37. SPEEDING UP SOLUTIONS

The process of dissolving a solute can be speeded up in several ways:

1. By heating the solvent.

2. By stirring the solvent.

3. By crushing or powdering the solute.

4. By a combination of these.

MATERIALS: two beakers, granulated sugar, sugar cubes, two tea bags, hot and cool water, stirrer, teaspoon, two tablespoons

- Fill both beakers nearly to the top, one with cool water and one with hot water. Place one sugar cube in each beaker and wait until the cube in the hot water dissolves. The cube in the tap water will still be partly undissolved.

- Fill both beakers nearly to the top, one with cool water and one with hot water. Dip a tea bag into both. Wait one minute and observe the difference.

- Fill both beakers nearly to the top with cool water. Place one sugar cube in each. Stir only one and observe that when its sugar cube is dissolved, sugar still remains undissolved in the other beaker.

- Fill both beakers nearly to the top with cool water. Place a teaspoon of sugar in one and a sugar cube in the other. Observe how the granulated sugar dissolves faster than the sugar cube. You may want to repeat this demonstration by crushing a sugar cube between two tablespoons and using the powder in place of the granulated sugar.

- Fill two beakers nearly to the top—one with cool water, the other with hot water. Add a sugar cube to both. Stir the hot water. Notice that the sugar dissolves more quickly.

38. SOLUTIONS CHANGE TEMPERATURE

Making solutions changes the temperature of the solute.

MATERIALS: concentrated sulfuric acid, ammonium nitrate, small test tube, two beakers, water, two thermometers

---
CAUTION! Wear goggles, apron, and gloves. Work away from students. Use fume hood, if available.

- Fill both beakers about halfway with tap water. Place a thermometer in each. Allow a minute for the thermometers to stabilize. Fill the small test tube three-quarters full of acid. Slowly pour the concentrated sulfuric acid into one beaker. Notice the change in temperature. The water becomes warmer by about 5°C.

Water   **Solution of Water and Sulfuric Acid**

- Fill both beakers about halfway with tap water. Place a thermometer in each. Allow a minute for the thermometers to stabilize. Pour some ammonium nitrate into one beaker, stir gently with the thermometer and observe its temperature drop about 5°C.

Water   **Solution of Water and Ammonium Nitrate**

39. SATURATED SOLUTIONS

Solutions can be weak, strong, and **saturated**. A solution is weak when more solute can be dissolved in it. A solution is strong when very little solute can be added. A solution is saturated when it can dissolve no more solute.

MATERIALS: balance, three beakers, water, sugar, balance, salt, stirrer, graduated cylinder

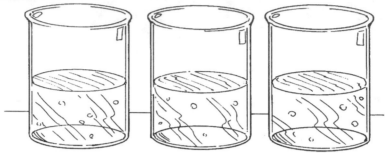

- Fill three beakers with 25 milliliters of tap water each. In the first one, place 1 gram of salt; in the second, 5 grams of salt; in the third, 10 grams of salt. Stir to dissolve the salt. Beaker #1 has a weak solution; beaker #2 has a stronger solution; and beaker #3 has the strongest solution. Keep adding salt to any one of the beakers, and stir until salt precipitates to the bottom and does not dissolve anymore. Now you have a saturated solution. You may wish to repeat this demonstration with granulated sugar.

40. SOLUTIONS: LOWER FREEZING POINT

The freezing of liquids occurs when liquids change into solids. For water, this happens at 0°C. Dissolving more solute in a solution lowers its freezing point. This property is used in everyday life. Antifreeze is added to a car's cooling system water to prevent it from freezing in very cold weather. Salt is added to sidewalks and streets to melt ice in winter. Once the water dissolves the salt, its freezing point is lowered and drops below 0°C.

MATERIALS: five cups, water, teaspoon, salt, balance, five thermometers, graduated cylinder, freezer

- Fill two cups three-quarters full of tap water and place a thermometer in each. Add a teaspoon of salt to one of them and stir until the salt is dissolved. Place both cups in a freezer. Check every five minutes for freezing and record the temperatures. The cup with the salt solution will show a freezing point well below 0°C.

- Take three cups and add to each of them 100 milliliters of water and a thermometer. In cup #1 dissolve 2 grams of salt; in cup #2, 5 grams of salt; and in cup #3, 10 grams of salt. Place the cups in a freezer. Every five minutes, check their temperatures and whether or not they are frozen. Cup #1 will freeze at –1°C, cup #2 at –3°C, and cup #3 at –6°C. There will be some minor variations due to altitude above sea level.

41. SOLUTIONS: HIGHER BOILING POINT

The boiling point of a liquid occurs when the liquid changes into a gas. For water, this point is at 100°C. Dissolving more solute in a solution increases the boiling point of the liquid. This property is used in everyday life. Antifreeze is added to a car's cooling system water to prevent its boiling over under severe heating conditions. Pasta, eggs, and other foods cook faster if salt is added to the water because the water boils at a higher temperature.

MATERIALS: hot plate, four beakers, salt, sugar, copper sulfate, baking soda, water, four thermometers, teaspoon, balance

- Fill four beakers with the same amount of water. In each of them, place a thermometer and two teaspoons of a different solute: salt, sugar, copper sulfate, and baking soda. Place the beakers on a hot plate, two at a time, and observe their boiling temperatures. They all will be above 100°C.

- Fill three beakers with 100 milliliters of water each. Add 5, 10, and 20 grams of salt to them, respectively. Place a thermometer in each beaker. Boil the water and observe the boiling points. They should be 101°C, 102°C, and 104°C, with some minor variation due to altitude above sea level.

42. SEPARATION OF SOLUTE

To separate the solute from a solution, several different approaches are used. Filtering out the solute does not work because the solute is molecular in size, too small to be blocked by the filter's pores. Only undissolved solute can be filtered out. Here are just a few methods for separating solute:

1. **Evaporation**: The solvent is boiled off (evaporated), and the solute is left behind.

2. **Deionizing**: ion exchange as in water softeners or dimineralizers. Minerals are drawn out of solution by, and form ionic bonds with, strong acids and bases. This process is used in many industries and in the water machines outside of many food markets.

3. **Flocculation (coagulation)**: Chemicals are added to precipitate some or all of the solute. This is one of the key ways municipal authorities treat drinking water.

4. **Osmosis**: The liquid is passed through a fine membrane. Osmosis is used for seawater desalinization and in appliances that purify home water.

5. **Flash freezing**: The solution is frozen suddenly and the ice is separated from the solute crystals. This is used to produce many products, such as freeze-dried coffee.

MATERIALS: beaker, copper sulfate, water, hot plate, 1-liter bottle of soda water, balloon, salt, teaspoon

- Fill the beaker three-quarters full of water. Add one teaspoon of copper sulfate, stir the liquid, and boil it until all the water has evaporated. The residue in the beaker is the copper sulfate. This is the same material you dissolved in the water earlier.

- To separate gas from solution with a liquid, take a liter bottle of soda water, remove its cap, and place an empty balloon over the opening. Let the bottle sit. As the bottle sits, the liquid warms up and the dissolved carbon dioxide comes out of solution, filling the balloon.

- Fill a beaker nearly to the top with tap water. Add 2 teaspoons of salt and mix. Let the mixture stand for about 10 days. The liquid will evaporate. All liquids evaporate if left uncovered.

43. DISTILLATION AND CONDENSATION

Distillation is the process by which the solvent and solute are separated and both are recovered. The process begins with the evaporation of the solvent. The gaseous solvent passes through cooling ducts, where the gas condenses into a liquid. **Condensation** is the change of a gas back into a liquid. If several solvents are mixed together, they can be separated by **fractional distillation**, since each boils at a different temperature. The liquid with the lowest boiling point starts evaporating first. After this liquid has evaporated, the one with the next highest boiling point evaporates, and so on. This process is used by the oil companies to separate crude petroleum into its many components, such as kerosene, gasoline, light oils, plastics, heating oil, heavy oils, and tar.

MATERIALS: hot plate, beaker, water, teaspoon, salt, ceramic plate or piece of glass, coffeepot

- Mix a teaspoon of salt in a beaker of water. Boil the beaker water. Place a piece of glass or a ceramic plate over the beaker, as a lid. On the bottom of the lid, water that has evaporated will condense.

- Fill a coffeepot with water and let it heat up. Lift the lid and show your students the condensation on the inside of the lid.

44. PAPER CHROMATOGRAPHY

Paper chromatography is a process that separates colors into their basic dyes. Paper is porous and absorbs liquids. If you dip the corner of a piece of paper in water, the paper acts as a wick. The water spreads, and the entire paper gets wet. This is **capillary action**. During the absorption of liquids by the paper, colors separate into their basic dyes. The heavier particles separate first and the lightest ones last. The paper with the separate color bands is a **chromatogram**.

MATERIALS: food colors, two paper towels, chlorophyll, paper, glass jar, water, scissors, masking tape, dropper

- Cut several strips of paper toweling about 8 inches long by 1 inch wide. Place a drop of food color about 2 inches from one end of a strip. Insert this strip end into a jar containing about 1 inch of clear water. Tape the other end of the strip to the top of the jar. Let the assembly stand for about 15 to 20 minutes. The basic colors will separate into their basic dyes, forming lines (bands). Green color will provide blue and yellow bands on the chromatogram.

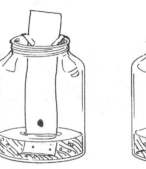

- Mix some red and blue food color. Place a drop of this mix on the paper and repeat the activity. You will get a clear separation of these two colors.

- Place some chlorophyll on the paper. You will get a clear separation of three chemicals—one red, one yellow, and one green. In some parts of the country, you may not get the green color if you extract your own chlorophyll in the fall.

45. CRYSTALS

Many solids have definite shapes. Observe sugar, copper sulfate, and salt with a magnifying glass. Their shapes are **crystals**. Diamonds are crystals of the element carbon. Crystals of materials have their own unique crystalline shapes. This physical property is helpful in their identification. Each crystallized material has its own index of refraction. Jewelers use small pencil-sized refraction meters to distinguish real diamonds from the semiprecious gem zircon. Crystal can be made with **supersaturated** solutions. Heating the solvent causes its molecules to move farther apart. This allows more solute to be dissolved, because there is more space between the molecules of the solvent. Boiling the solvent results in a supersaturated solution. If more solute is added until some of it precipitates, the solution is supersaturated.

MATERIALS: glass jar, pot, pencil, water, string, button, granulated sugar, copper sulfate, beaker, detergent, hot plate, measuring cup

- Wash out the jar thoroughly. Boil the string and the button in water for a few minutes to kill all bacteria. Boil a cup of water in the pot and remove it from the fire. Dissolve in it all the sugar you can by stirring. You will have made a supersaturated solution. Since the liquid is hot, it will dissolve more solute than it would at room temperature. Tie a button to one end of the piece of string, and the middle of the pencil to the other end. Dip the wet string in the sugar solution. Gently lower

the string into the jar and use the
pencil as a support. Turn the pencil
to adjust the height of the button. It
needs to be about one-half inch from
the bottom of the jar. Let the assembly
stand for several days. You will notice
that sugar crystals (**rock candy**) are
growing on the string.

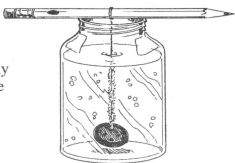

- Heat a nearly full beaker of water to
a boil. Add enough copper sulfate to
make it a saturated solution. Let the beaker cool. When cool, add just a
few crystals of copper sulfate to the now supersaturated solution. A few
days later, observe how more crystals of copper sulfate have formed
and risen to the top of the supersaturated solution.

46. SUSPENSIONS—CLOUDY LIQUIDS

Solutions are mixtures that are clear and homogeneous. Suspensions are
mixtures that are cloudy. In solutions, the solute is molecular in size. In suspensions, particles do not dissolve. A ready-to-use salad dressing is mixed before
use. After a few minutes, it separates and suspended particles settle to the
bottom. Many foods and medicines are suspensions and need to be shaken prior
to their use. Suspensions can be separated by settling, filtering, or centrifuging.
Settling and centrifugation settle particles on the bottom of the container
according to size, from the largest to the smallest.

COMPARISON OF LIQUID SUSPENSIONS AND SOLUTIONS

SUSPENSION	SOLUTION
Cloudy	Clear
Two or more substances are mixed.	Two or more substances are mixed.
Usually settles out on standing.	Does not settle out on standing.
Particles are larger than molecular in size.	Particles are molecular in size.
Particles do not dissolve.	Particles dissolve.

MATERIALS: two beakers, soil, starch, flask, filter paper, stirrer, centrifuge,
water, test tube

- Mix some soil in a beaker nearly full of water. Notice how cloudy the mixture becomes. Let the soil particles settle overnight on the bottom.

- Mix some starch in a beaker nearly full of water. Filter out the starch.

- Take some soil mixed with water, place it in a test tube, and centrifuge it. You will get the same result as with slow settlement, but in just a few minutes.

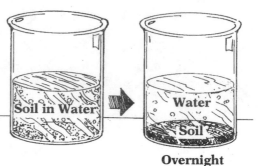

47. DETERGENTS: EMULSIFIERS

Detergents and soaps are used for cleaning. They surround the dirt particles with a fine film, or emulsion. One can easily recognize **emulsification** because the liquid turns a milky white.

MATERIALS: glass, water, teaspoon, liquid detergent, salad oil

- Fill a glass halfway with water and top it with 1 to 2 centimeters of salad oil. While standing, the water and oil will separate into two distinct layers. Stir them together and let them stand a few minutes. Again they will separate. Add a teaspoon of detergent and stir them together. The mixture turns white (emulsification), and the oil and water do not separate anymore. If they do, add a little bit more detergent.

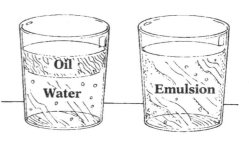

48. Detergents: Wetting Agents

Detergents make water wetter by being wetting agents. Wetting agents break the electrical bonds holding water molecules together. Alcohol is a wetting agent.

MATERIALS: string, scissors, two glasses, liquid detergent, water, teaspoon, pepper

- Cut the string into 3- to 4-centimeter pieces. Fill both glasses nearly to the top with water and add one teaspoon of detergent to one. Place several pieces of string in both glasses. In the glass with the wetting agents, the strings sink almost immediately, while the strings in the plain water take quite a long time. You may want to repeat this activity and time the wetting action of water on different materials.

- Fill a glass nearly to the top with water. Sprinkle pepper on the water. Place one drop of detergent on the surface and observe the pepper either sink or float to the edges.

> **CAUTION!** Make sure that you rinse out the glasses thoroughly between uses.

49. Making Mayonnaise—Colloids

Mayonnaise is yet another form of emulsion or colloid. A colloid is a mixture in which extremely small particles of a substance are mixed and dispersed in another substance. The particles are groups of molecules, atoms, or ions and are smaller than those in a regular suspension. In colloidal suspensions, molecules in motion bounce around larger particles in suspension. This is **Brownian motion**.

MATERIALS: glass, salad oil, vinegar, egg, microscope, slide, carmine dye, stirrer

- Mix three parts of oil with one part of vinegar. When mixed together, they will separate. Add the white of an egg and mix together by stirring rapidly. Now you have a colloidal solution.

- Mix some carmine dye with water. Examine it under a microscope. Notice how the carmine particles move about in a random fashion. This movement, Brownian motion, is caused by the collision of carmine dye particles with water molecules.

EXAMPLES OF COLLOIDS

	GAS	LIQUID	SOLID
Gas	XXXXXXXXXXX	whipped cream, shaving cream, spray paint	soap floats (air bubbles) plastic foam
Solid	smog, smoke in air	color in water	XXXXXXXXXXX
Liquid	cloud, fog, mist	emulsions, milk	jams, jellies

50. MAKING SOAP

Soap was made at home during the colonial period. Here is a chance for you to do something that links your students to the past.

MATERIALS: can of lye (sodium hydroxide, NaOH), fat and grease, vinegar, hot plate, 10-quart or larger pan, stirring spoon (wooden, plastic, or stainless steel), 2-gallon electric cooking pot or enamelware, water, measuring cup, perfume, color, Pyrex dishes or boxes, wax paper, knife

---

CAUTION! Lye is caustic. Wear goggles, apron, and gloves. Keep students at a distance. Follow safety procedures.

- For several days, collect enough fat and grease to half-fill the pan.

1. Clean the grease: Melt it in the pan with 2 to 3 quarts of water. Bring it to a boil and stir frequently. Let it cool until you can lift out the fat. Repeat the procedure several more times to remove salts and other sediments.

2. To dissolve the lye, use the electric cooking pot. Place the container on the ground for all to observe from a safe distance. Carefully read the label on the lye container. *Slowly* stir the

1 qt. Cold Water

lye into 1 quart of cold water. In this process the lye will react with the water and get very hot. Stir *very slowly* to avoid any splatter.

CAUTION! Should any lye get on you, neutralize it immediately with vinegar and rinse generously with water.

---

3. As soon as the lye solution feels lukewarm on the bottom of the pot, slowly add to it the melted lukewarm grease. Continue stirring until the mixture stiffens to the consistency of honey.

4. At this time, add coloring and perfume (if desired).

5. Continue stirring the pot for 20 to 30 minutes, or until the soap becomes the consistency of fudge.

6. Pour the soap into forms lined with wax paper —Pyrex dishes or boxes. Let it stand until it is hard enough to be cut into 4-inch squares.

7. Let the squares dry in sunshine for a couple of weeks. Turn them over daily so that they harden.

8. When ready, cut the soap into smaller bars and give them to your students to take home.

51. COAGULATION

Coagulation (flocculation) is the process of adding chemicals to suspensions to get suspended particles to clump together and settle faster. Larger particles settle faster than smaller ones. Coagulation is a common method used by water treatment plants to purify water and remove residual sediments, after the water has been filtered through a bed of sand and gravel.

MATERIALS: aluminum sulfate $Al_2(SO_4)_3$ (alum), ammonium hydroxide NH_4OH, test tube, stirrer, two beakers, water, clay or plain soil, teaspoon

- Mix together a small amount of alum and ammonium hydroxide. Fill two beakers nearly to the top with water and add some clay or plain soil to them. Stir both of them well, so that the clay is in suspension. Add a small amount of the chemical mix to one beaker. While standing, the one with the coagulating chemicals settles faster. The one without chemicals will need at least overnight to settle.

Solution of
Aluminum Sulfate
Ammonium Hydroxide

Water

Clay

52. Acids

Acid is a substance that if added to water increases the concentration of hydronium ions—an ion group made up of a water molecule and a hydrogen ion. Acids react with metals, producing hydrogen gas. Acids turn litmus red (pink). Litmus is an indicator that turns colors in the presence of acids and bases. Acids are found in citrus fruit, in sour milk, in vinegar, in the stomach, etc. Acids are sour to the taste and a few can cause severe body tissue damage. Soda water contains carbon dioxide. Carbon dioxide dissolves in water and becomes carbonic acid. Bubbles of carbon dioxide are visible in soda, beer, and sparkling wines. Here are a few important acids:

Acid	Formula	Where Found, Uses
Hydrochloric acid	HCl	In stomach, aids digestion
Sulfuric acid	H_2SO_4	Industry, for metals, plastics, etc.
Boric acid	H_3BO_3	Eyewash, insect control
Acetic acid	$HC_2H_3O_2$	Vinegar, photography
Carbonic acid	H_2CO_3	Soda water, beer, sparkling wines
Nitric acid	HNO_3	Used in making jewelry, explosives, medicines

MATERIALS: thistle funnel, rubber stopper with two holes, glass tubing, flat-bottomed flask, glass jar, pie tin with hole, water dish, water, diluted hydrochloric acid, graduated cylinder, zinc pellets, splint, matches

- In this activity, you will assemble the necessary apparatus for water displacement, to collect hydrogen gas. (See illustration.) Place the zinc pellets on the bottom of the flask. Pour in 50 milliliters of hydrochloric acid. Add more if needed, until you have sufficient hydrogen gas to test. Perform the pop test:
Light a splint and place it inside the jar. You will hear a loud pop.

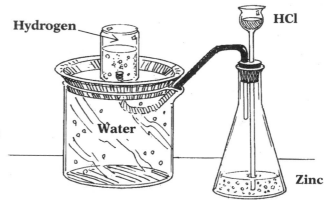

53. BASES

Certain metals react with water and form **bases** and hydrogen. Bases are substances that contain the hydroxyl ion OH. Bases are bitter to the taste, slimy (at times), slippery, and react with acids. Bases turn red litmus to blue. Soap, baking soda, milk of magnesia, ammonia, and most detergents are examples of bases. Drāno™, the powder or liquid used to unclog drains, contains sodium hydroxide (NaOH), a very strong and caustic base. Sodium hydroxide is known as lye and is used to make soap.

MATERIALS: beaker, water, baking soda, vinegar, test tube, teaspoon, basin

- Perform the following over a sink or a basin. Fill the beaker halfway with water and add two teaspoons of baking soda. Stir the soda so that it is well mixed. Fill the test tube about halfway with vinegar. Pour the vinegar into the baking soda. Notice the reaction and the bubbles. This is the typical reaction by bases to acids.

54. LITMUS AND OTHER INDICATORS

Litmus is an organic indicator. **Organic** means that the indicator contains the element carbon and comes from formerly living matter. An **indicator** changes color in the presence of certain chemicals. Litmus reacts to acids and bases. Other indicators react to pH, minerals in water, and other chemical conditions. Litmus red appears pink. Litmus blue appears as a weak violet, almost sky blue.

MATERIALS: three litmus red strips, three litmus blue strips, baking soda, vinegar, water, three beakers, teaspoon

- Prepare the three beakers as follows: Fill each of them halfway with water. Add a teaspoon of baking soda to one, several teaspoons of vinegar to the next, and leave the third one alone. Now you have one that is a base, one that is an acid, and one that is near neutral. Place a litmus red strip into each beaker. The base turns the red to blue, and the acid and the tap water do nothing. Next place a litmus blue strip into each beaker. The base does not change the litmus blue; the acid changes the blue to red; and the tap water does nothing. In a neutral substance, neither litmus red nor litmus blue changes color.

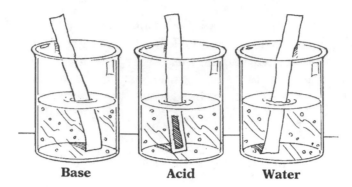

Base   **Acid**   **Water**

Here is a summary for litmus and other indicators:

INDICATOR	COLOR IN ACIDS	COLOR IN BASES
Litmus	red	blue
Bromthymol blue	yellow	blue
Methyl orange	red	yellow
Phenolphthalein	clear, no color	pink
Congo red	blue	red

55. INDICATOR—BROMTHYMOL BLUE (BTB)

MATERIALS: bromthymol blue concentrate, liquid dishwashing detergent, ammonia, Alka Seltzer™ tablets, water, large beaker, two tumblers or beakers, overhead projector

Bromthymol blue or **BTB**, an indicator, is available as a liquid, a solid, and as treated paper strips. It is yellow in the acid state, pale green when neutral, and blue when in the base state. Alka Seltzer has a slight lemon content (citric acid), which makes it acidic. It is designed to neutralize a person's stomach acid only partially. The acidity of Alka Seltzer will cause the BTB to turn yellow. The chemical reaction of the tablet with water, produces carbon dioxide, the fizz.

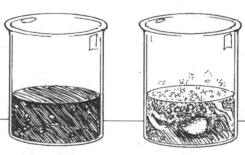

- Prepare a solution of BTB, by adding BTB concentrate to a liter- or quart-sized beaker filled

with water. Add a few drops of liquid dish detergent and a few drops of ammonia to turn the liquid deep blue. Pour about two inches of this liquid into two tumblers or beakers. Place half an Alka Seltzer tablet in one glass and observe the reaction. Use the other glass as a control. Bottom-light the glasses with the overhead projector.

56. STARCH TEST —IODINE

Starch is a carbohydrate. Carbohydrates contain the elements carbon, hydrogen, and oxygen. Examples are starch, sugar, potatoes, vegetables, fruit, cereals, and legumes. Starch is used extensively to stiffen objects, such as writing paper, paper plates, clothes, and also as a filler in many foods.

MATERIALS: Lugol's solution (iodine), sheet of writing paper, paper plate, slice of bread, cracker, slice of potato

- Add a drop of Lugol's solution to a slice of bread, a cracker, or a slice of potato. If the brown liquid, Lugol's solution, turns blue-black, then the substance contains starch. Repeat the test with plain writing paper and a paper plate. (Some of the thinner and cheaper paper plates are stiffened with starch.)

57. NEUTRALIZATION

Some substances are neutral; they do not turn litmus blue to red and/or litmus red to blue. The pH of a neutral substance is 7. Neutral substances do not contain hydronium ions or hydroxide ions. **Neutralization** is the reaction between acids and bases that forms water and salts. People take bases as medicine to neutralize stomach upsets due to too much acid.

MATERIALS: hydrochloric acid, vinegar, eyedropper or burette, graduated 100-milliliter cylinder, phenolphthalein, baking soda, water, two beakers

$$HCl \; + \; NaOH \; \longrightarrow \; NaCl \; + \; H_2O$$
$$Acid \; + \; Base \; \longrightarrow \; Salt \; + \; Water$$

- Pour 10 milliliters of vinegar into a beaker. Add phenolphthalein to the vinegar. This is the acid solution. Prepare a strong base solution by adding baking soda to water in the other beaker. Add the base drop by drop to the acid. Count the number of base drops that are required to turn the acid suddenly to a light pink. Repeat the activity with the hydrochloric acid. This demonstration will show that a stronger acid needs more base to be neutralized.

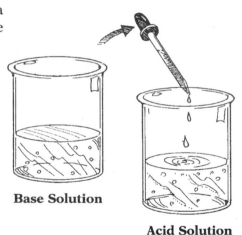

Base Solution

Acid Solution

58. ELECTROLYTES—CONDUCTIVITY OF WATER

Distilled water (water without dissolved minerals—acids, bases, and salts) is a poor conductor of electricity. If some acid, base, or salt is added to the distilled water, it becomes a good conductor of electricity. Substances that make water a good conductor of electricity are **electrolytes**. Some electrolytes conduct electricity better than others. Substances such as sugar, which do not conduct electricity when added to water, are nonelectrolytes. There are two types of conductivity apparatus: those having a bulb that lights up to varying degrees of brightness, and those having a meter. The former are more visual, the latter more practical. Both types employ low-voltage batteries for safety reasons.

MATERIALS: conductivity apparatus, glacial acetic acid, sodium hydroxide, salt, four beakers, distilled water, stirrer

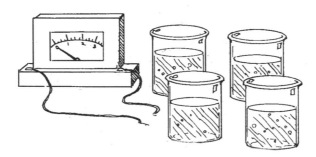

- Pour distilled water into one beaker, glacial acetic acid into another, sodium hydroxide into another, and salt into the last one. Test all four to make the point that they all are poor conductors of electricity. Place 250 milliliters of distilled water into the three beakers containing the acid, the base, and the salt. Stir them to get a good mixture. Again, test these three beakers for electroconductivity. They will all conduct electricity well.

59. CONSERVATION OF MATTER

The law of **conservation of matter** states that during a chemical reaction, matter cannot be either created or destroyed. If you burn a piece of paper, the black ashes appear to have less mass than the original paper. The paper is made up of carbon, oxygen, hydrogen, and some minerals. As the paper burns, it produces water vapor and carbon dioxide. All that is left are the mineral ashes. In the following demonstrations, you will burn matches and a candle and conserve all the by-products of combustion. The first demonstration is simple; the second is more sophisticated and complex.

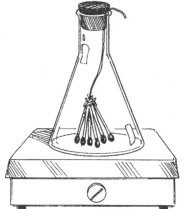

MATERIALS: hot plate, pressure flask, stopper, wooden matches, balance, tongs, sewing thread

- Place a dozen matches on the bottom of a pressure flask by hanging them in a bundle with the sewing thread. Insert the stopper tightly, and measure the mass of the flask. Place the flask on the hot plate and heat it until the matches ignite and burn. Again, measure the mass of the pressure flask. It will be the same.

MATERIALS: large balance, base and vacuum bell with stopper top, 25 inches of bell wire, wire stripper, sewing thread, 12 V battery or equivalent DC power supply, candle, matches, rocket engine igniter, vacuum sealing wax

The rocket engine igniter is available in most toy or hobby stores that sell model rockets. It is inexpensive. Buy a pack of six.

- Follow these steps:

1. Light the candle. Use a few drops of candle wax to fasten it in a standing position in the center of the vacuum bell base.

2. Extinguish the candle flame.

3. Attach to the candle wick a match head and the tip of the rocket engine igniter. Use a dental rubber band or a few pieces of sewing thread to accomplish this.

4. Strip from both ends of the bell wires $\frac{1}{2}$ inch of insulation. Connect one end of each bell wire (fold back and squeeze it) to each end of the engine igniter.

5. Lead the wires out of the jar through the stoppered top.

6. Seal the bell jar and stopper with sealing wax to prevent any connection between the inside and the outside.

7. Place the entire assembly on the balance and find out its mass down to the last decimal place. Leave it on the balance.

8. Recheck that the mass has not changed. Connect the free ends of the wires to the battery or power supply. At this point, the igniter will ignite the match head and the wick. The candle will burn until it exhausts the oxygen in the bell jar's limited air supply. Notice that the balance did not change; all the materials of combustion were trapped in the jar.

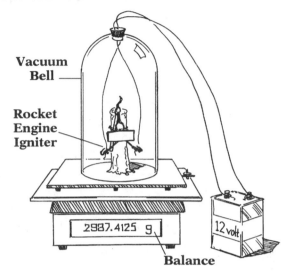

60. CORROSION OF METALS

Corrosion is a chemical change that occurs in metals exposed to gases and liquids. It is the wearing away of metals. Metals combine with chemicals in the air and in water to form new compounds. Notice how a shiny copper penny turns to a dull color, an iron nail rusts, copper seems to get a green coating (verdigris) with time, aluminum objects lose their shine, and silver turns black. Slow oxidation is what causes iron to rust. Combining iron with oxygen yields iron oxide. The process is usually slow. Combining aluminum with oxygen yields aluminum oxide. Combining lead with oxygen yields lead oxide. Several oxides have specific colloquial names: (1) iron oxide—rust; (2) silver oxide—silver tarnish. Advertisements correctly state that aluminum will not rust. Rusting is a specific property of iron. Aluminum will oxidize, however. Gold and platinum do not oxidize. For this reason, gold is used to coat electric contacts and other critical surfaces where oxidation is not acceptable, such as computer board contacts, crucial missile components, and biomedical equipment.

MATERIALS: steel wool, soap, iron nail (not galvanized), two test tubes, paper clip, beaker, water, grease pencil, new nail, rusty nail, lead sinker, small dish, splint, matches

- Show your students a rusty nail and a new nail. Demonstrate that the nail rusted slowly. Place an iron nail in a test tube with water and let it stand for a few days. It will rust.

- Scratch a lead sinker with a nail, and show your students oxidized and nonoxidized lead. Have them examine the sinker after a few minutes; lead oxidizes rapidly. Lead oxides have been used in paints as corrosion inhibitors for centuries. They have been banned due to lead's extreme toxicity. Pass the lead sinker around in a small dish. If students touch the sinker, follow the caution.

> **CAUTION!** After handling lead, wash hands immediately.

- Follow these steps:

1. Take a small amount of steel wool, enough to fill about a third of the test tube, and wash it well with soap to remove oils. These are added in manufacturing to prevent it from rusting.

2. Fasten the steel wool inside the test tube with the paper clip. Invert the test tube and place it in a beaker filled halfway with water.

3. Mark the water level inside the test tube with a grease pencil. Leave the assembly in place and observe the slow rusting of the steel wool. Notice also the rising water level inside the test tube. The steel wool is using up the oxygen.

Clip

4. When the activity ends, mark the new water level. As the steel wool oxidizes (rusts), it uses up the oxygen in the test tube. Notice that it will be approximately 20% of the original air volume.

5. Remove the test tube from the beaker, keeping it tightly closed with your thumb. Run a splint test to show that there is no oxygen left in the test tube.

61. PROTECTING METALS FROM CORROSION

To protect metals from becoming weak by corrosion, several strategies are used. Metals are alloyed with other metals to provide them with the desirable qualities. Metal objects, such as car bumpers and sink faucets, are chrome-plated. Others are covered with paint or similar films to separate them from the environment. Protective sacrificial plates are added in watercraft, water heaters, etc., where **galvanic corrosion** (caused by weak electric currents) occurs.

MATERIALS: beaker, water, vinegar, clear nail polish, lubricating oil or petroleum jelly, several iron (not galvanized) nails, one galvanized nail

Select all nails of about the same size.

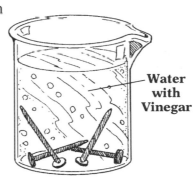

- In a beaker nearly full of water, place some vinegar to speed up the rusting process. In the liquid, place four iron nails: one that has been thoroughly coated with oil or petroleum jelly, one that has been coated with clear nail polish, one that is uncoated, and one that is galvanized. Let the assembly stand for a few days; then examine it carefully. The galvanized nail will not rust. The iron nail will rust. The coated nails will resist rust, depending on how carefully you have coated them.

Water with Vinegar

62. OXIDATION OF PAPER

Burning is a process of rapid oxidation. When oxidation takes place at an extremely fast rate, an explosion occurs. Oxidation is a chemical reaction.

MATERIALS: piece of paper, matches, sink with faucet or container with water

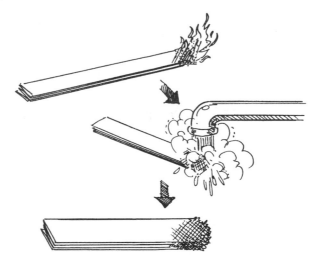

- Fold a piece of paper into a narrow strip and light it with a match. When about half has burned, stop the fire with water. Point out that this is rapid oxidation.

63. CITRUS BATTERY

MATERIALS: lemon or other citrus fruit, galvanometer or voltmeter (VOM), copper penny, quarter, paper towel, aluminum foil, salt, water, small glass

- Cut two slits in the citrus fruit and insert a coin into each. Make certain that the coins are separated and do not meet inside the fruit. Connect one lead of the galvanometer to each coin and show how electric current flows.

- Cut a piece of aluminum foil about 3 by 5 centimeters or larger. Cut a piece of paper towel slightly larger than the aluminum foil. Soak the paper in salt-water solution and place it over the aluminum foil. Place the penny on the paper, so that it sticks up past the edge of the paper. Fold the paper aluminum sandwich over the coin. Connect the galvanometer to the aluminum and the copper penny, and it will show the flow of electric current. The two different metals become electrodes. You have a model of a dry-cell battery. Dry-cell batteries have an internally moist electrolyte, despite being called dry. When this electrolyte dries out, the battery becomes dead. In the same way, your battery will work as long as the paper is wet. Your single-cell battery can be reactivated by again wetting the paper towel in a salt solution. The widely sold potato clock works on the same principle. It has two different metal electrodes that are pushed into the potato. The potato juice acts as the electrolyte. The liquid crystal display clock requires so little current that a two-cell potato battery is sufficient. For the potato you can substitute citrus fruit, soil, soda, etc., because their internal moisture acts as the electrolyte.

64. METALS: ELECTROMOTIVE FORCE (EMF)

The reactivity of an element is based upon its ability to gain or lose electrons used in bonding. (See also Demonstration 70, page 60.) Some elements are very reactive, some less reactive, and some totally unreactive. The reactivity series is a listing of elements (usually metals) in descending order of reactivity. The differences in reactivity are used to produce electricity and to protect metals from corrosion. Elements will displace only elements with a lower reactivity. Elements that are at the top of the reactivity series have the following characteristics:

1. Greater reactivity.

2. Better reducing agents (remove oxygen in some chemical reactions).

3. Greater ability to lose electrons to form ions (electromotive force, EMF).

4. Greater displacement power.

5. Greater negative electrode potential.

REACTIVITY SERIES

Lithium	**–3.06V**	Most active
Potassium		
Calcium		
Sodium		
Magnesium		
Aluminum		
Zinc		
Iron		
Tin		
Lead		
Hydrogen	**0V**	
Copper		
Iodine		
Silver		
Mercury		
Bromine		
Chlorine	**+1.36V**	Least active

MATERIALS: two test tubes, copper sulfate, iron sulfate, iron nail (not galvanized), copper strip or 2-inch piece of #12 bare copper wire, water, test tube holder

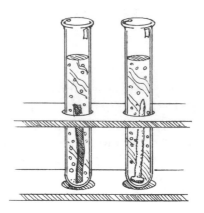

- Place a piece of copper in a test tube containing water and iron sulfate. After letting stand five minutes, note that nothing has happened. Copper does not displace an element with a higher EMF.

- Place an iron nail in a solution of copper sulfate. After several minutes, the solution turns green, and the nail appears to be coated with copper. The iron displaced the copper. Here is this simple displacement reaction:

$$Fe + CuSO_4 \rightarrow Cu + FeSO_4$$

Iron + Copper sulfate $\rightarrow$ Copper + Ferrous sulfate

65. BATTERY: AN ELECTROCHEMICAL CELL

When different metals are immersed in an electrolyte, an electric current flows, creating an electrochemical cell. A battery is the combination of several electrochemical cells. Electrochemical cells have either a reversible or nonreversible chemistry. The reversible type, such as the automobile battery, reverses the chemical reaction during the charging cycle. Then the battery is ready to go again. The nonreversible battery ceases to function when it runs out of chemicals to react. An example is an ordinary throwaway flashlight battery. A crucial point to note is that a chemical battery does not store electrical energy; it stores only chemicals that will react. The chemical reaction pushes the electrons in the circuit. An electron flow is current. Most wet-cell batteries use diluted acids as electrolytes. Many higher-quality dry cells use a paste that is a strong base, thus their generic name "alkaline."

MATERIALS: battery demonstration kit or beaker, two different metal plates such as zinc and copper, wires, galvanometer, vinegar (sulfuric acid optional), baking soda, water

- Connect the galvanometer to the two metal strips with the wire, and dip the plates into a water-vinegar solution in the beaker. Sulfuric acid may be substituted for the vinegar; however, it must be used cautiously, following all safety procedures. Be careful that the two metal plates do not touch each other. You will observe bubbles in the liquid on the copper plate, and the galvanometer will indicate current flow. Here is what happens: The zinc plate oxidizes, losing electrons that become zinc ions. These ions enter the solution. The electrons then move through the wire and through the meter to the copper plate. This move-ment of electrons is by definition electric current. Hydrogen ions in the vinegar pick up the electrons from the copper strip. In this process, hydrogen becomes a bubbling gas on the copper plate. You may elect to repeat this demonstration using a solution of baking soda and water as the electrolyte. It would illustrate alkaline batteries.

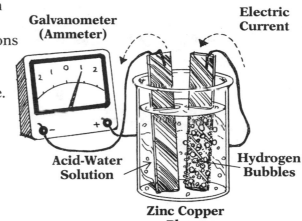

- Mention that some of your students may have experienced a mild electric shock from placing a metal object, such as aluminum foil (from a baked potato), in their mouth. The metal plus their fillings and saliva (an electrolyte) made a battery. These are galvanic currents.

66. HARD AND SOFT WATER

Water that moves over the surface or seeps underground dissolves many minerals. Water that contains dissolved salts of magnesium and calcium is hard water. Hard water requires much soap to form suds, because most of the soap combines with the ions in the water and is wasted. Industry and homes use water-softening devices to treat water. In the softening process, the insoluble calcium ion is replaced by a soluble sodium ion. This is the reason soft water requires very little soap or detergent. Hard water leaves calcium carbonate (lime) deposits inside water pipes and appliances. These deposits reduce the water flow by gradually building a thick coating inside the pipes and damaging delicate appliance valves. When dishes are washed with hard water, the water leaves stains on glassware and silverware. Lime (a base) is the ring around bath-tubs and toilets. It is the white coating on shower doors. Lime can be washed away by using acidic cleansers or vinegar.

MATERIALS: green soap, USP (obtain from a pharmacy), dropper bottle, two test tubes, test tube holder, soft or distilled water, hard (tap) water

- Mix 1 part of green soap to 8 to 10 parts of water in the dropper bottle. The greater the dilution of soap, the more drops of soap you will use. Fill both test tubes halfway with water, using soft water in one and hard water in the other. Put 2 to 3 drops of soap in both test tubes and shake them. The soft water will form plenty of suds, while the hard water will change slightly to a milky color with barely any suds. Continue adding soap drops to the hard water. After each drop, shake the test tube. If suds appear, see if they stay for three minutes. If they do not, continue adding soap until they do. Compare the number of drops needed for the hard water to those used for the soft water. This demonstration is a good student investigation.

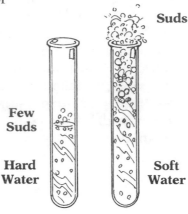

67. Atomic Data—Periodic Table— Bohr Diagram

This demonstration is the *first of three*. The three demonstrations need to be done in their *correct order*. To describe an atom, people use the **periodic table**. This table provides much information, but you need only certain essentials: name of element, symbol, atomic mass, atomic number, and electron shells (quanta) configuration. In the Appendix, there is a special interpreted periodic table (Chart of Elements, Page 92). The following is a summary of atomic basics:

1. **Atomic mass** is the number of protons plus the number of neutrons in the nucleus of an atom.

2. **Atomic number** is the number of protons in an atom.

3. Orbital **shells** (quanta-orbitals) are listed alphabetically starting with the letter *K*. Each shell can contain from one to a maximum number of electrons. That number is its quantum number.

4. **Protons** are positive charges, **neutrons** are neutral charges, and **electrons** are negative charges.

5. For every proton (+) in the nucleus, there is a matching electron (–) in orbit.
   The relative masses are: Electron   1
                               Proton   1843
                               Neutron   1844

- By looking at the relative mass of the subatomic particles, one can conclude that any particle in the nucleus of the atom is about 2000 times more massive than any one in orbit. This defines an atom as having a very massive nucleus with mostly empty space around it. If you were able to become miniaturized and take a walk through an atom, chances are that you would never see an electron and you would miss the nucleus altogether. An atom is mostly empty space.

- Look at the periodic table in the Appendix on page 92 and prepare your own chart. Round off atomic masses to the nearest whole number. Determine the number of neutrons in the following manner:

Example:
Lanthanum   La

Atomic mass   139
Atomic number   − 57
Number of neutrons = 82

Examples:
From Chart of Elements

ATOMIC #	NAME	SYMBOL	ATOMIC MASS	ELECTRONS (IN SHELLS)
				K,L,M,N,O,P,Q
57	Lanthanum	La	138.9055	2,8,18,18,9,2

Your Prepared Chart

NAME	SYMBOL	ATOMIC NUMBER	ATOMIC MASS	NUMBER OF PROTONS	NUMBER OF NEUTRONS	NUMBER OF ELECTRONS	SHELLS K,L,M,N, O,P,Q
Lanthanum	La	57	139	57	139−57=82	57	2,8,18,18, 9,2

68. Bohr Diagram of Atom

This is the *second of three* demonstrations. They need to be done *in sequential order.* The **Bohr diagram** of an atom provides a visual model and information on how protons, neutrons, and electrons are arranged within an atom. The illustration shows a Bohr model for the atom charted in the last demonstration.

The negative numbers represent the number of electrons in that particular shell or orbit. It is far more expedient to draw the symbol and number than actually draw tiny circles with +, –, and N embedded. Furthermore, we are never certain where the electrons are at any one time. We only know how many are there. In this demonstration, you will complete the diagram of an atom and abbreviate it, to make it easier to draw.

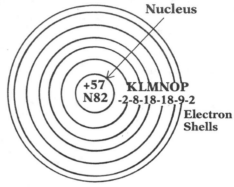

- The completed Bohr diagram needs the calculations and its diagram:

Lanthanum La

Atomic mass	139
Atomic number	–57
Number of neutrons	= 82

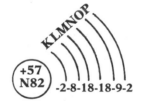

Here the shells were abbreviated to simplify the drawing. This permits many Bohr diagrams to fit on a single page. This is a good place to assign your students the first 10 elements of the periodic table. Ask them to do a complete Bohr diagram of each, including its illustration. Please note that hydrogen does not have a neutron.

69. Bohr Model of an Atom

This is the *third of three* demonstrations. These need to be done *in sequence.* In this demonstration, you will build either a full or a half model of an atom. Full models look great. Half models are useful for atoms that have many components. They require much less construction material.

MATERIALS: flexible copper or galvanized wire, small polystyrene balls ($\frac{1}{2}$ inch), one larger polystyrene ball (3–5 inches), rectangular piece of polystyrene about 20 × 20 × 1–2 inches, tempera paint, brushes, paper clips, toothpicks, glue, paper, index card, string or sewing thread, sealing tape, wire cutter, pen

- To make a full model: Take the large polystyrene ball and skewer it with a paper clip bent to form a hook. Next, using toothpicks, fasten into it the correct number of small painted balls to represent the neutrons and protons. Do not have them touching each other. Make certain that neutrons, protons, electrons, and the nucleus have different colors. All elements of one kind, like electrons, need to be of the same color. Make as many wire loops as needed. In our example of Lanthanum, you would need six loops. Make the smallest (K shell) slightly larger than the nucleus, then L > K, M > L, N > O, etc. With the shell wire, skewer the correct number of electron balls and spread them out. Tie the loop closed. Attach the shells and the nucleus with string or sewing thread, so that each shell can rotate independently. On the bottom, attach an index card with the complete Bohr diagram and a legend, to define the colors of the model.

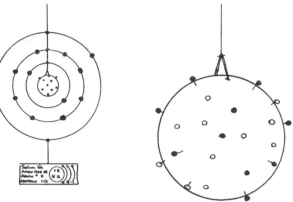

- If you wish to make a model of an element that has many shells, make a half model. A half model has a base and you see only half of the atom. Make certain that neutrons, protons, electrons, and the nucleus are different colors. All elements of one kind, such as electrons, need to be of the same color. Using several toothpicks and a drop of glue, mount in the center of the polystyrene board half the large ball. Use toothpicks to mount small half-balls to represent neutrons and protons. Use only a few to obtain visual impact. Cut wires for shells. These will be of varying lengths, with *K* the shortest. With the wire, skewer a few electron balls, fold the wire over the nucleus, and press its two ends into the polystyrene board. The next shell will be longer, higher than *K* and at an angle, to provide a three-dimensional effect. When the half model is completed, place an index card on the base with the Bohr diagram and a color legend. Place a small flag on each wire with the shell letter.

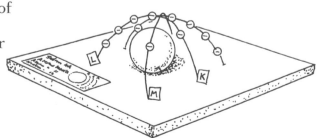

Assigning this project to your students provides an excellent review of atomic concepts.

70. VALENCE—IONS

When elements gain, lose, or share electrons with other elements or compounds, there is an electrical bond. This is the true cosmic glue of the universe that keeps all objects from falling apart into neat piles of basic elements. Atoms combine following precise rules. If the outermost shell of an element has 8 electrons, the shell is complete. If the shell has 4, 5, 6, and 7 electrons, it tries to gain the missing number of electrons to become a complete shell of 8 electrons. If a shell has 1, 2, 3, and 4 electrons, it tries to give them away or share them. If a shell has 4 electrons only, at times it will gain 4 electrons, and at times it will give away its own and it will also share them. The group of elements with 4 electrons in its outermost shell is called **amphoteric**. They are used to make semiconductors that do and do not conduct electric currents.

The number of electrons that an atom can borrow, lend, or share is the **valence number**. If an element has one electron to lend, it has a +1 **positive valence**. If an element would like to borrow one electron, it has a valence of –1, or **negative valence**.

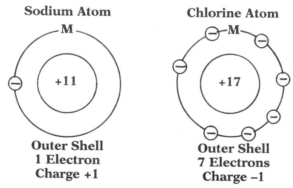

Sodium Atom	Chlorine Atom
Outer Shell 1 Electron Charge +1	Outer Shell 7 Electrons Charge –1

Sodium has one electron to give, and chlorine needs one to fill its shell. When this transaction is completed, one has a compound called sodium chloride (salt) and this union is a **chemical change**. When atoms lend or borrow electrons, they become electrically charged and turn into **ions**. If an atom lends electrons, it becomes a **positive ion**. If an atom gains electrons, it becomes a **negative ion**. Metals usually become positive ions and nonmetals become negative ions. When the sodium and chlorine combine, sodium becomes a positive ion and chlorine a negative ion. Note that some elements have more than one valence.

- Show your students the diagrams of sodium and chlorine atoms. Then complete the diagram as shown below. First show the migrating electron. Then connect the two outermost shells. Now 8 electrons can orbit both the sodium and chlorine atoms in a superorbit.

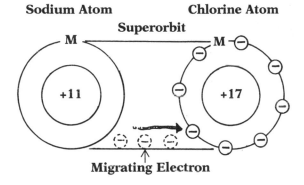

71. ELECTROVALENCE—COVALENCE

Atoms combine in two specific ways:

1. They lend and borrow electrons: **electrovalence**.

2. They share electrons: **covalence**.

- Show your students these concepts with the illustrations provided:

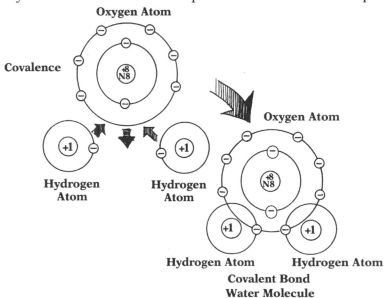

Here is a summary of electrovalent and covalent compounds:

ELECTROVALENT COMPOUNDS	COVALENT COMPOUNDS
Atoms form ions.	Atoms do not form ions.
Atoms gain and lose electrons.	Atoms share electrons.
Atoms fill outer shell.	Atoms fill outer shell.
Atoms gain and lose electrons.	No electrons are gained or lost.

72. FORMULA MASS

In order to make and study compounds, you need to know the mass of how much of each element must be added to result in just the right amount. Each atom has its own mass, based on that of carbon being 12 units. Since hydrogen is $\frac{1}{12}$ of carbon, then its mass is 1 unit. The unit can be any unit as long as it is the same throughout the discussion: gram, kilogram, ounce, pound, etc. This, in very practical terms, provides us with means of measuring masses for chemicals in the laboratory. **Formula mass** is arrived at as follows:

FORMULA	ELEMENT	ATOMIC MASS		SUBSCRIPT		FORMULA MASS
Pb	Pb	207	×	1	=	207
H_2	H	1	×	2	=	2
H_2O	H	1	×	2		2+
	O	16	×	1		16+
					=	18
Al_2O_3	Al	27	×	2		54+
	O	16	×	3		48+
					=	102

- Have your students figure out the formula mass for a few compounds: F_2 fluorine, Cl_2 chlorine, NaCl sodium chloride, Ag_2O silver oxide, $Zn_3(PO_4)_2$ zinc phosphate, and Fe_2S_3 ferric sulfide.

73. SUPERABSORBENCY AND POLYMERS

Superabsorbent substances are used in high absorbency diapers, in feminine hygiene products, in alkaline batteries, in potting soil, in water beds, in magic tricks, and in fuel filtration material to remove moisture from automobile and jet fuels. There are many other uses besides this brief listing. **Polymers** are substances made up of long molecules. The long molecules consist of many monomers (small molecules) bonded together in a repeating sequence. **Monomers** are relatively small molecules that combine to form polymers. **Sodium polyacrylate** is made by polymerizing a mixture of sodium acrylate and acrylic acid. The superabsorbent substance works by osmotic pressure. The polymer acts as a permeable membrane. The difference in sodium concentration between the inside of the polymer and the outside water causes the water to rush inside, trying to get to an equilibrium of sodium ions inside and outside the polymer. The amount of electrolytes in the water greatly affects the amount of water that can be absorbed by a unit amount of polymer. It will absorb 800 times its own weight in distilled water. It will absorb only 300 times its own weight in tap water due to the ion concentration in water. It will absorb only 60 times its weight of 0.9% sodium chloride (salt) solution, nearly the same concentration as found in urine.

MATERIALS: pencil, distilled water, teaspoon, sodium polyacrylate (Waterlock™), salt, paper or polystyrene cup

Source for sodium polyacrylate: Flint Scientific Inc., P.O. Box 219, Batavia, IL 60510, phone (708) 879-6900 / fax (708) 879-6962. Sodium polyacrylate comes in 25 g, 100 g, and 500 g, and it costs about $16.30 for 500 g (part # W0014).

Pour 100 milliliters of distilled water into a paper or polystyrene cup. Add 0.125 grams of sodium polyacrylate to the other cup ($\frac{1}{2}$ teaspoon or full teaspoon, if your water has a high mineral content). Pour the water into the cup containing the powder. The key to this demonstration is to pour the water into the cup containing the powder and to stall for about 10 to 15 seconds, asking students what will happen, to give time for the gel to form. The water will be absorbed almost immediately by a process called gelling. Take the pencil and starting midway from the top, make horizontal holes through the cup. No water will spill out. Repeat by making holes closer to the bottom. Nothing will come out. Finally make a hole in the bottom of the cup. Nothing will come out. At this time, push the pencil straight through the cup and take

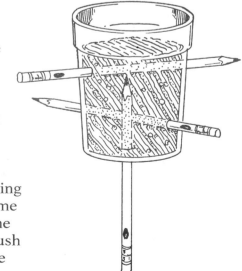

it out from the top. Pour the gel into a beaker. You can break the gel by adding salt to the polymer and gently mixing it. It will appear as if it melted. Salt will decrease its water absorbency.

> **CAUTION!** Sodium polyacrylate is not toxic. However, it may irritate the eyes and the nose by drying them up. Dispose of excess powder or gel in the trash, *not* in a sink. Do not return any powder to its container.

74. CHEMICAL FORMULAS

A **chemical formula** is an expression using symbols for the various elements and compounds. In the example provided, both hydrogen and oxygen come as doubles. They are **diatomic elements**, that is, they travel in pairs. Other diatomic elements are Br_2 (bromine), F_2 (fluorine), Cl_2 (chlorine), I_2 (iodine), O_2 (oxygen), H_2 (hydrogen) and N_2 (nitrogen). In the last step, the 2's are added in front of the hydrogen and water molecule to balance what goes in with what comes out.

Hydrogen + Oxygen Yields Water

$$H + O \rightarrow$$

$$H_2 + O_2 \rightarrow H_2O$$
Subscripts

$$2H_2 + O_2 \rightarrow 2(H_2O)$$
Coefficients

- Go over the following definitions with your students to prepare them for writing chemical formulas.

KEY DEFINITIONS FOR CHEMICAL FORMULAS

1. **Valence** is the potential combining power of elements and groups of elements, using hydrogen (+1) as a standard.

2. **Valence electrons** are those electrons that are either gained, lost, or shared. They are the electrons in the outermost orbit of an atom.

3. **Valence number** is the number of electrons gained, lost, or shared. An element or radical can have more than one valence number. In chemical formula writing, valence is written as a Roman numeral above the symbols.

4. **Formula** is an abbreviation for either an element or a compound, and it stands for one molecule. *Examples:* NaCl, H_2O, $C_{12}H_{22}O_{11}$, O_2. The element has one symbol, while the compound has several. The exception are elements that have two letters. *Example:* C (carbon) and Co

(cobalt) are elements, CO (carbon monoxide) is a compound. The second capital letter is the only clue that another element is there. H_2SO_4 is a compound (sulfuric acid) and so is HCl (hydrochloric acid).

5. **Atom** is the basic building block of matter that makes up molecules.

6. **Symbol** is the abbreviation for the name of an element and stands for one atom. *Examples:* Na, Cl, S, R, U, O, Co, Ca, Sn. The second letter must always be lowercase.

7. **Radical** is a group of atoms that is moved as a group. Think of it as a transparent shoe box with objects inside. You can see what is inside but you cannot change it.

8. **Subscript** is a small number written after the symbol to show that more than one of a particular atom is used. *Example:* H_2O. If a subscript follows a group of atoms (usually in parentheses), then it means that the whole package (radical) is taken more than one time. *Example:* $Ca(OH)_2$, calcium hydroxide, the OH radical is used twice.

75. WRITING CHEMICAL FORMULAS

Before starting this demonstration, become familiar with the Bohr model of an atom. See Demonstration 68, page 58.

Valence equation rules resolve the sticky problem of drawing Bohr diagrams to figure out superorbits for complex molecules. In this demonstration, you will illustrate how valence equations are arrived at. While this may appear complicated, in reality it is not. Take it one step at a time and you will find it pleasantly comfortable.

The purpose of a valence equation is to establish the exact proportions or numbers for each element/radical that are needed to make a new molecule. It is the same as developing the exact proportions for the ingredients of a kitchen recipe. Kitchen recipes sometimes combine single ingredients with several premixed ingredients. In chemistry, single elements combine with groups, and groups combine with other groups. Have students visualize mixing eggs with cheese, milk, and green peppers for an omelet, or mixing water with pancake mix (ready-made mix of many ingredients). An example of groups mixing with groups is combining pancake mix with Ovaltine™ mix.

The **key definitions** needed for this activity are in Demonstration 74, page 64. The Formula Writing Exercises, pages 68–69, can be used as a guide for student assignments. You can use a check mark whenever students combine a particular new molecule. NOTE: The law of conservation of matter states that matter cannot be either created or destroyed; it merely changes form. Likewise, once the valence equation is arrived at, then one must balance both sides of it to make sure that what goes in comes out. Balancing equations is omitted, for it is beyond the scope of this book.

RULES FOR VALENCE EQUATIONS

Use the formula writing exercises that follow these rules as a resource:

1. Write the element or group with the positive valence first, then the negative one. The positive valence elements/groups are listed in the first column. The negative valence elements/groups are written across the top of the page.

2. Write valence numbers as Roman numerals above and to the right of each element or group as a superscript.

3. Crisscross the values. The valence number becomes a subscript for the opposite group or element. Now they are written as Arabic numbers. If you were to draw a thin line between the superscripts and subscripts, a cross would be formed. You may want to do so initially until your students gain fluency with the process.

4. Discard both subscripts (only the ones you have written) if they are the same number. Do not write a subscript if it is a 1. A symbol for an element stands for one atom, and the numeral 1 makes it redundant.

5. Use parentheses to enclose groups only if you need to use subscripts on their outside. If you do not, drop the parentheses. Under no circumstances mix subscripts inside parentheses with those on the outside. Consider groups as packages, and take as many of these as needed. You can look on the inside of the package but you cannot change it.

6. Combine the names provided under the elements/groups in the correct order. The names provided in the exercises are the final names for the new compounds, not those of the parent elements/groups.

EXAMPLES:

$$\overset{+I}{Ag_1} + \overset{+I}{Cl_1} ===> AgCl \text{ Silver-chloride (Drop subscripts; they are equal.)}$$

$$\overset{+I}{Na_1} + \overset{+I}{(OH)_1} ===> NaOH \text{ Sodium-hydroxide (Drop subscripts; they are equal. Drop brackets, not needed.)}$$

$$\overset{+II}{Zn_2} + \overset{-II}{S_2} ===> ZnS \text{ Zinc-sulfide (Drop subscripts; they are equal.)}$$

+II   –I
$Cu_1 + (NO_3)_2 ===> Cu(NO_3)_2$ Copper nitrate (1 atom of copper and 2 molecules of nitrite)

+III   –I
$Fe_1 + (HSO_4)_3 ===> Fe(HSO_4)_3$ Ferric bisulfate (1 atom of iron and 3 molecules of bisulfate)

+II   +III
$Ca_3 + (PO_4)_2 ===> Ca_3(PO_4)_2$ Calcium phosphate (3 atoms of calcium and 2 molecules of phosphate)

+I   –III
$(NH_4)_3 + (PO_4)_1 ===> (NH_4)_3PO_4$ Ammonium phosphate (Drop parentheses; 3 molecules of ammonia and 1 of phosphate.)

FORMULA WRITING EXERCISES PAGE 1 OF 2

| VALENCE | –I | –I | –I | –I | –I | –I |
| Formula | Cl | (NO$_3$) | (OH) | (NO$_2$) | (HCO$_3$) | (HSO$_4$) |
Name (final)	Chloride	Nitrate	Hydroxide	Nitrite	Bicarbonate	Bisulfate
Hg +I Mercurous						
Ag +I Silver						
Na +I Sodium						
K +I Potassium						
(NH$_4$) +I Ammonium						
Zn +II Zinc						
Cu +II Copper						
Fe +II Ferrous						
Hg +II Mercurous						
Mg +II Magnesium						
Ca +II Calcium						
Ba +II Barium						
Pb +II Lead						
Fe +III Ferric						
Al +III Aluminum						

FORMULA WRITING EXERCISES   PAGE 2 OF 2

VALENCE Formula Name (final)	$-II$ O Oxygen	$-II$ (SO_3) Sulphite	$-II$ S Sulfide	$-II$ (CO_3) Carbonate	$-III$ (PO_3) Phosphite	$-III$ (PO_4) Phosphate
Hg +I Mercurous						
Ag +I Silver						
Na +I Sodium						
K +I Potassium						
(NH_4) +I Ammonium						
Zn +II Zinc						
Cu +II Copper						
Fe +II Ferrous						
Hg +II Mercurous						
Mg +II Magnesium						
Ca +II Calcium						
Ba +II Barium						
Pb +II Lead						
Fe +III Ferric						
Al +III Aluminum						

Appendix

BRIEF HISTORY OF CHEMISTRY

Chemistry is a science that studies atoms. It started in ancient Egypt and was carried from North Africa into Spain by the Moors. It spread across Europe under the name of alchemy. Alchemists tried to change ordinary metals into gold. They believed that if they found a substance called the philosopher's stone, they could make this transmutation. Though they did not achieve transmutation, they did make valuable discoveries over a period of 1000 years. Some looked for the universal solvent, a material that dissolves nearly everything. They failed to realize that water was it. Others looked for the *elixir vitae*, a substance that would extend life.

J.J. Becher (1635–1682), Basil Valentine, Geber, and Philippus Paracelsus (1493?–1541) were among the outstanding alchemists looking for ways to fight diseases. Paracelsus helped chemistry become part of medicine. In the eighteenth century, Antoine-Laurent Lavoisier (1743–1794) made chemistry an independent science.

In chemistry, matter is considered to be anything that takes up space and has mass. Matter is classified as elements, mixtures, and compounds. If matter is divided and subdivided until one reaches the final unbreakable chunk, one reaches an atom. Two or more of the same atoms together are an element. Scientists have discovered more than 106 different elements, including 92 basic elements. Elements are divided into two groups: metals and nonmetals. Metals are further subdivided into two subgroups:

1. Noble (gold, silver, platinum, etc.)

2. Base (tin, lead, mercury, iron, copper, etc.)

Dmitri Ivanovich Mendeléev (1834–1907), a Russian chemist, helped develop a periodic table of elements. He organized the known elements of his day in a special way on his chart. The empty spaces predicted the existence and general properties of many unknown elements. His chart led to the discovery of most of the remaining elements over the next few decades.

Count Amadeo Avogadro (1776–1856) figured out that equal volumes of all gases at the same temperature and pressure have the same number of atoms. There are 6.02×10^{23} (602,000,000,000,000,000,000,000) atoms in a standard mass unit, the gram-molecule.

Madam Marie Sklodowska Curie (1867–1934; Nobel Prize, 1903, 1911), a Polish-born French physicist, discovered radium, a highly radioactive element.

Albert Einstein (1879–1955; Nobel Prize, 1921), a German-born American physicist, revolutionized the modern thought on atomic energy and the structure of matter. He proved in his famous equation $E = mc^2$ that on an atomic level, matter was the same as energy.

Niels Bohr (1885–1962; Nobel Prize, 1922), a Danish physicist, developed the Bohr theory of the atom. He theorized that in hydrogen there is one proton in the nucleus and one electron in a near circular orbit. Energy is emitted if the atom moves from one energy level to a lower energy level.

Werner Karl Heisenberg (1901–1976; Nobel Prize, 1932), a German physicist, provided an extensive description of atomic energy levels in the field of quantum mechanics. He is most famous for his uncertainty principle.

Enrico Fermi (1901–1954), Leo Szilard (1898–1964), J. Robert Oppenheimer (1904–1967), and many others helped use the knowledge of atoms to make nuclear energy work for the modern world.

The most remarkable thing about these and many other scientists is that not a single one of them had ever seen an atom. Yet Avogadro counted them, Einstein figured out their energy equivalent, Bohr described their inner geography, Heisenberg developed the theory of energy levels, and Mendeléev correctly predicted the existence of many yet undiscovered elements. Photographs of actual atoms have become available to scientists only in the seventies. When new and more accurate investigative tools become available to explore the basic mysteries of nature, science makes revisions to its current theories.

DENSITY OF LIQUIDS

	approx. gm/cm^3 at 20°C
Acetone	0.79
Alcohol (ethyl)	0.79
Alcohol (methyl)	0.81
Benzene	0.90
Carbon disulfide	1.29
Carbon tetrachloride	1.56
Chloroform	1.50
Ether	0.74
Gasoline	0.68
Glycerin	1.26
Kerosene	0.82
Linseed oil (boiled)	0.94
Mercury	13.6
Milk	1.03
Naphtha (petroleum)	0.67
Olive oil	0.92
Sulfuric acid	1.82
Turpentine	0.87
Water 0° C	0.99
Water 4° C	1.00
Water - sea	1.03

ALTITUDE, BAROMETER, AND BOILING POINT

altitude (approx. ft)	barometer reading (cm of mercury)	boiling point (° C)
15,430	43.1	84.9
10,320	52.0	89.8
6190	60.5	93.8
5510	62.0	94.4
5060	63.1	94.9
4500	64.4	95.4
3950	65.7	96.0
3500	66.8	96.4
3060	67.9	96.9
2400	69.6	97.6
2060	70.4	97.9
1520	71.8	98.5
970	73.3	99.0
530	74.5	99.5
0	76.0	100.0
- 550	77.5	100.5

SPECIFIC GRAVITY

gram /cm^3 at 20° C.

Agate	2.5-2.6	Granite*	2.7	Polystyrene	1.06
Aluminum	2.7	Graphite	2.2	Quartz	2.6
Brass*	8.5	Human body - normal	1.07	Rock salt	2.1-2.2
Butter	0.86	Human body - lungs full	1.00	Rubber (gum)	0.92
Cellural cellulose acetate	0.75	Ice	0.92	Silver	10.5
Celluloid	1.4	Iron (cast)*	7.9	Steel	7.8
Cement*	2.8	Lead	11.3	Sulfur (roll)	2.0
Coal (anthracite)*	1.5	Limestone	2.7	Tin	7.3
Coal (bituminous)*	1.3	Magnesium	1.74	Tungsten	18.8
Copper	8.9	Marble*	2.7	Wood Rock Elm	0.76
Cork	0.22-0.26	Nickel	8.8	Balsa	0.16
Diamond	3.1-3.5	Opal	2.1-2.3	Red Oak	0.67
German Silver	8.4	Osmium	22.5	Southern Pine	0.56
Glass (common)	2.5	Paraffin	0.9	White Pine	0.4
Gold	19.3	Platinum	21.4	Zinc	7.1

*Non homogeneous material. Specific gravity may vary. Table gives average value.

CONVERSIONS OF TEMPERATURE CELSIUS–FAHRENHEIT

C°	F°	C°	F°	C°	F°	C°	F°	C°	F°	C°	F°
250	482.00	200	392.00	150	302.00	100	212.00	50	122.00	0	32.00
249	480.20	199	390.20	149	300.20	99	210.20	49	120.20	-1	30.20
248	478.40	198	388.40	148	298.40	98	208.40	48	118.40	-2	28.40
247	476.60	197	386.60	147	296.60	97	206.60	47	116.60	-3	26.60
246	474.80	196	384.80	146	294.80	96	204.80	46	114.80	-4	24.80
245	473.00	195	383.00	145	293.00	95	203.00	45	113.00	-5	23.00
244	471.20	194	381.20	144	291.20	94	201.20	44	111.20	-6	21.20
243	469.40	193	379.40	143	289.40	93	199.40	43	109.40	-7	19.40
242	467.60	192	377.60	142	287.60	92	197.60	42	107.60	-8	17.60
241	465.80	191	375.80	141	285.80	91	195.80	41	105.80	-9	15.80
240	464.00	190	374.00	140	284.00	90	194.00	40	104.00	-10	14.00
239	462.20	189	372.20	139	282.20	89	192.20	39	102.20	-11	12.20
238	460.40	188	370.40	138	280.40	88	190.40	38	100.40	-12	10.40
237	458.60	187	368.60	137	278.60	87	188.60	37	98.60	-13	8.60
236	456.80	186	366.80	136	276.80	86	186.80	36	96.80	-14	6.80
235	455.00	185	365.00	135	275.00	85	185.00	35	95.00	-15	5.00
234	453.20	184	363.20	134	273.20	84	183.20	34	93.20	-16	3.20
233	451.40	183	361.40	133	271.40	83	181.40	33	91.40	-17	1.40
232	449.60	182	359.60	132	269.60	82	179.60	32	89.60	-18	-0.40
231	447.80	181	357.80	131	267.80	81	177.80	31	87.80	-19	-2.20
230	446.00	180	356.00	130	266.00	80	176.00	30	86.00	-20	-4.00
229	444.20	179	354.20	129	264.20	79	174.20	29	84.20	-21	-5.80
228	442.40	178	352.40	128	262.40	78	172.40	28	82.40	-22	-7.60
227	440.60	177	350.60	127	260.60	77	170.60	27	80.60	-23	-9.40
226	438.80	176	348.80	126	258.80	76	168.80	26	78.80	-24	-11.20
225	437.00	175	347.00	125	257.00	75	167.00	25	77.00	-25	-13.00
224	435.20	174	345.20	124	255.20	74	165.20	24	75.20	-26	-14.80
223	433.40	173	343.40	123	253.40	73	163.40	23	73.40	-27	-16.60
222	431.60	172	341.60	122	251.60	72	161.60	22	71.60	-28	-18.40
221	429.80	171	339.80	121	249.80	71	159.80	21	69.80	-29	-20.20
220	428.00	170	338.00	120	248.00	70	158.00	20	68.00	-30	-22.00
219	426.20	169	336.20	119	246.20	69	156.20	19	66.20	-31	-23.80
218	424.40	168	334.40	118	244.40	68	154.40	18	64.40	-32	-25.60
217	422.60	167	332.60	117	242.60	67	152.60	17	62.60	-33	-27.40
216	420.80	166	330.80	116	240.80	66	150.80	16	60.80	-34	-29.20
215	419.00	165	329.00	115	239.00	65	149.00	15	59.00	-35	-31.00
214	417.20	164	327.20	114	237.20	64	147.20	14	57.20	-36	-32.80
213	415.40	163	325.40	113	235.40	63	145.40	13	55.40	-37	-34.60
212	413.60	162	323.60	112	233.60	62	143.60	12	53.60	-38	-36.40
211	411.80	161	321.80	111	231.80	61	141.80	11	51 80	-39	-38.20
210	410.00	160	320.00	110	230.00	60	140.00	10	50.00	-40	-40.00
209	408.20	159	318.20	109	228.20	59	138.20	9	48.20	-41	-41.80
208	406.40	158	316.40	108	226.40	58	136.40	8	46.40	-42	-43.60
207	404.60	157	314.60	107	224.60	57	134.60	7	44.60	-43	-45.40
206	402.80	156	312.80	106	222.80	56	132.80	6	42.80	-44	-47.20
205	401.00	155	311.00	105	221.00	55	131.00	5	41.00	-45	-49.00
204	399.20	154	309.20	104	219.20	54	129.20	4	39.20	-46	-50.80
203	397.40	153	307.40	103	217.40	53	127.40	3	37.40	-47	-52.60
202	395.60	152	305.60	102	215.60	52	125.60	2	35.60	-48	-54.40
201	393.80	151	303.80	101	213.80	51	123.80	1	33.80	-49	-56.20

CONVERSIONS OF TEMPERATURE FAHRENHEIT–CELSIUS

F⁰	C°	F⁰	C°	F⁰	C°	F⁰	C°	F⁰	C°	F⁰	C°
250	121.11	200	93.33	150	65.56	100	37.78	50	10.00	0	-17.78
249	120.56	199	92.78	149	65.00	99	37.22	49	9.44	-1	-18.33
248	120.00	198	92.22	148	64.44	98	36.67	48	8.89	-2	-18.89
247	119.44	197	91.67	147	63.89	97	36.11	47	8.33	-3	-19.44
246	118.89	196	91.11	146	63.33	96	35.56	46	7.78	-4	-20.00
245	118.33	195	90.50	145	62.78	95	35.00	45	7.22	-5	-20.56
244	117.78	194	90.00	144	62.22	94	34.44	44	6.67	-6	-21.11
243	117.22	193	89.44	143	61.67	93	33.89	43	6.11	-7	-21.67
242	116.67	192	88.89	142	61.11	92	33.33	42	5.56	-8	-22.22
241	116.11	191	88.33	141	60.56	91	32.78	41	5.00	-9	-22.78
240	115.56	190	87.78	140	60.00	90	32.22	40	4.44	-10	-23.33
239	115.00	189	87.22	139	59.44	89	31.67	39	3.89	-11	-23.89
238	114.44	188	86.67	138	58.89	88	31.11	38	3.33	-12	-24.44
237	113.89	187	86.11	137	58.33	87	30.56	37	2.78	-13	-25.00
236	113.33	186	85.56	136	57.78	86	30.00	36	2.22	-14	-25.56
235	112.78	185	85.00	135	57.22	85	29.44	35	1.67	-15	-26.11
234	112.22	184	84.44	134	56.67	84	28.89	34	1.11	-16	-26.67
233	111.67	183	83.89	133	56.11	83	28.33	33	0.56	-17	-27.22
232	111.11	182	83.33	132	55.56	82	27.78	32	0.00	-18	-27.78
231	110.56	181	82.78	131	55.00	81	27.22	31	-0.56	-19	-28.33
230	110.00	180	82.22	130	54.44	80	26.67	30	-1.11	-20	-28.89
229	109.44	179	81.67	129	53.89	79	26.11	29	-1.67	-21	-29.44
228	108.89	178	81.11	128	53.33	78	25.56	28	-2.22	-22	-30.00
227	108.33	177	80.56	127	52.78	77	25.00	27	-2.78	-23	-30.56
226	107.78	176	80.00	126	52.22	76	24.44	26	-3.33	-24	-31.11
225	107.22	175	79.44	125	51.67	75	23.89	25	-3.89	-25	-31.67
224	106.67	174	78.89	124	51.11	74	23.33	24	-4.44	-26	-32.22
223	106.11	173	78.33	123	50.56	73	22.78	23	-5.00	-27	-32.78
222	105.56	172	77.78	122	50.00	72	22.22	22	-5.56	-28	-33.33
221	105.00	171	77.22	121	49.44	71	21.67	21	-6.11	-29	-33.89
220	104.44	170	76.67	120	48.89	70	21.11	20	-6.67	-30	-34.44
219	103.89	169	76.11	119	48.33	69	20.56	19	-7.22	-31	-35.00
218	103.33	168	75.56	118	47.78	68	20.00	18	-7.78	-32	-35.56
217	102.78	167	75.00	117	47.22	67	19.44	17	-8.33	-33	-36.11
216	102.22	166	74.44	116	46.67	66	18.89	16	-8.89	-34	-36.67
215	101.67	165	73.89	115	46.11	65	18.33	15	-9.44	-35	-37.22
214	101.11	164	73.33	114	45.56	64	17.78	14	-10.00	-36	-37.78
213	100.56	163	72.78	113	45.00	63	17.22	13	-10.56	-37	-38.33
212	100.00	162	72.22	112	44.44	62	16.67	12	-11.11	-38	-38.89
211	99.44	161	71.67	111	43.89	61	16.11	11	-11.67	-39	-39.44
210	98.89	160	71.11	110	43.33	60	15.56	10	-12.22	-40	-40.00
209	98.33	159	70.56	109	42.78	59	15.00	9	-12.78	-41	-40.56
208	97.78	158	70.00	108	42.22	58	14.44	8	-13.33	-42	-41.11
207	97.22	157	69.44	107	41.67	57	13.89	7	-13.89	-43	-41.67
206	96.67	156	68.89	106	41.11	56	13.33	6	-14.44	-44	-42.22
205	96.11	155	68.33	105	40.56	55	12.78	5	-15.00	-45	-42.78
204	95.56	154	67.78	104	40.00	54	12.22	4	-15.56	-46	-43.33
203	95.00	153	67.22	103	39.44	53	11.67	3	-16.11	-47	-43.89
202	94.44	152	66.67	102	38.89	52	11.11	2	-16.67	-48	-44.44
201	93.89	151	66.11	101	38.33	51	10.56	1	-17.22	-49	-45.00

UNITS CONVERSIONS AND CONSTANTS

FROM	TO	X BY
Acres	Square feet	43560
Acres	Square meters	4046.8564
Acre-feet	Cu-feet	43560
Avogadro's number	6.02252×10^{23}	
Barrel (US dry)	Barrel (US liquid)	0.96969
Barrel (US liq.)	Barrel (US dry)	1.03125
Bars	Atmospheres	0.98692
Bars	Grams/sq.cm.	1019.716
Cubic feet	Acre-feet	2.2956841×10^{-5}
Cubic feet	Cu.centimeters	28316.847
Cubic feet	Cu.meters	0.028316984
Cubic feet	Gallons (US liquid)	7.4805195
Cubic feet	Quarts (US liquid)	29.922078
Cubic inches	Cu. centimeters	16.38706
Cubic inches	Cu. feet	0.0005787037
Cubic inches	Gallons (US liquid)	0.004329004
Cubic inches	Liters	0.016387064
Cubic inches	Ounces (US, fluid)	0.5541125
Cubic inches	Quarts (US. liquid)	0.03463203
Cubic meters	Acre-feet	0.0008107131
Cubic meters	Barrels (US liquid)	8.386414
Cubic meters	Cubic feet	35.314667
Cubic meters	Gallons (US liquid)	264.17205
Cubic meters	Quarts (US Liquid)	1056.6882
Cu. yards	Cu. Cm.	764554.86
Cu. yards	Cu. feet	27
Cu. yards	Cu. inches	46,656
Cu. yards	Liters	764.55486
Cu. yards	Quarts (US Liquid)	807.89610
Days (mean solar)	Days (Sidereal)	1.0027379
Days (mean solar)	Hours (mean solar)	24
Days (mean solar)	Hours (sidereal)	24.065710
Days (mean solar)	Years (Calendar)	0.002739726
Days (mean solar)	Years (sidereal)	0.0027378031
Days (mean solar)	Years (tropical)	0.0027379093
Days (sidereal)	Days (mean solar)	0.99726957
Days (sidereal)	Hours (mean solar)	23.93447
Days (sidereal)	Hours (sidereal)	24
Days (sidereal)	Minutes (mean solar)	1436.0682
Days (sidereal)	Minutes (sidereal)	1440
Days (sidereal)	Second (sidereal)	86400
Days (sidereal)	Years (calendar)	0.0027322454
Days (sidereal)	Years (sidereal)	0.0027303277

UNITS: CONVERSIONS AND CONSTANTS *(continued)*

FROM	TO	X BY
Days (sidereal)	Years (tropical)	0.0027304336
Decibels	Bels	0.1
Decimeters	Feet	0.32808399
Decimeters	Inches	3.9370079
Degrees	Minutes	60
Degrees	Radians	0.017453293
Degrees	Seconds	3600
Dekameters	Feet	32.808399
Dekameters	Inches	393.70079
Dekameters	Yards	10.93613
Decimeters	Feet	0.32808399
Decimeters	Inches	3.9370079
Decimeters	Meters	0.1
Degrees	Circles	0.0027777
Degrees	Minutes	60
Degrees	Quadrants	0.0111111
Degrees	Radians	0.017453293
Degrees	Seconds	600
Dekaliters	Pecks (U.S.)	1.135136
Dekameters	Pints (U.S. dry)	19.16217
Dekameters	Centimeters	1000
Dekameters	Feet	32.808399
Dekameters	Inches	393.70079
Dekameters	Yards	10.93613
Fathoms	Centimeters	182.88
Fathoms	Feet	6
Fathoms	Inches	72
Fathoms	Meters	1.8288
Fathoms	Miles (naut. Int.)	0.00098747300
Fathoms	Miles (statute)	0.001136363
Fathoms	Yards	2
Feet	Centimeters	30.48
Feet	Fathoms	0.166666
Feet	Furlongs	0.00151515
Feet	Inches	12
Feet	Meters	0.3048
Feet	Microns	304800
Feet	Miles (naut. Int.)	0.00016457883
Feet	Miles (statute)	0.000189393
Feet	Rods	0.060606
Feet	Yards	0.333333
Gallons (U.S. liq.).	Acre-feet	3.0688833×10^{-6}

UNITS: CONVERSIONS AND CONSTANTS *(continued)*

FROM	TO	X BY
Gallons (U.S. liq.)	Barrels (U.S. liq.)	0.031746032
Gallons (U.S. liq.)	Bushels (U.S.)	0.10742088
Gallons (U.S. liq.)	Cu. centimeters	3785.4118
Gallons (U.S. liq.)	Cu. feet	0.133680555
Gallons (U.S. liq.)	Cu.inches	231
Gallons (U.S. liq.)	Cu. meters	0.0037854118
Gallons (U.S. liq.)	Cu. yards	0.0049511317
Gallons (U.S. liq.)	Gallons (U.S. dry)	0.85936701
Gallons (U.S. liq.)	Gallons (wine)	1
Gallons (U.S. liq.)	Gills (U.S.)	32
Gallons (U.S. liq.)	Liters	3.7854118
Gallons (U.S. liq.)	Ounces (U.S. fluid)	128
Gallons (U.S. liq.)	Pints (U.S. liq.)	8
Gallons (U.S. liq.)	Quarts (U.S. liq.)	4
Grains	Carats (metric)	0.32399455
Grains	Drams (apoth. or troy)	0.016666
Grains	Drams (avdp.)	0.036671429
Grains	Grams	0.06479891
Grains	Milligrams	64.79891
Grains	Ounces (apoth. or troy)	0.0020833
Grains	Ounces (avdp.)	0.0022857143
Grams	Carats (metric)	5
Grams	Drams (apoth. or troy)	0.25720597
Grams	Drams (avdp.)	0.56438339
Grams	Dynes	980.665
Grams	Grains	15.432358
Grams	Ounces (apoth. or troy)	0.032150737
Grams	Ounces (avdp.)	0.035273962
Gravitational constant	Cm./(sec. X sec.)	980.621
Gravitational constant = G	dyne cm^2 g^{-2}	6.6732(31) X 10^{-8}
Gravitational constant	Ft./(sec. X sec.)	32.1725
Gravitational constant = G	N m^2 kg^{-2}	6.6732(31) X 10^{-11}
Gravity on Earth =1	Gravity on Jupiter	2.305
Gravity on Earth =1	Gravity on Mars	0.3627 Equatorial
Gravity on Earth =1	Gravity on Mercury	0.3648 Equatorial
Gravity on Earth =1	Gravity on Moon	0.1652 Equatorial
Gravity on Earth =1	Gravity on Neptune	1.323 ± 0.210 Equatorial
Gravity on Earth =1	Gravity on Pluto	0.0225 ± 0.217 Equatorial
Gravity on Earth =1	Gravity on Saturn	0.8800 Equatorial
Gravity on Earth =1	Gravity on Sun	27.905 Equatorial
Gravity on Earth =1	Gravity on Uranus	0.9554 ± 0.168

UNITS: CONVERSIONS AND CONSTANTS *(continued)*

FROM	TO	X BY
		Equatorial
Gravity on Earth =1	Gravity on Venus	0.9049 Equatorial
Hectares	Acres	2.4710538
Hectares	Sq. feet	107639.10
Hectares	Sq. meters	10000
Hectares	Sq. miles	0.0038610216
Hectares	Sq. rods	395.36861
Hectograms	Pounds (apoth or troy)	0.26792289
Hectograms	Pounds (avdp.)	0.22046226
Hectoliters	Cu. cm.	1.00028×10^5
Hectoliters	Cu. feet	3.531566
Hectoliters	Gallons (U.S. liq.)	26.41794
Hectoliters	Ounces (U.S.) fluid	3381.497
Hectoliters	Pecks (U.S.)	11.35136
Hectometers	Feet	328.08399
Hectometers	Rods	19.883878
Hectometers	Yards	109.3613
Horsepower	Horsepower (electric)	0.999598
Horsepower	Horsepower (metric)	1.01387
Horsepower	Kilowatts	0.745700
Horsepower	Kilowatts (Int.)	0.745577
Horsepower-hours	Kw.-hours	0.745700
Horsepower-hours	Watt-hours	745.700
Hours (mean solar)	Days (mean solar)	0.0416666
Hours (mean solar)	Days (sidereal)	0.041780746
Hours (mean solar)	Hours (sidereal)	1.00273791
Hours (mean solar)	Minutes (mean solar)	60
Hours (mean solar)	Minutes (sidereal)	60.164275
Hours (mean solar)	Seconds (mean solar)	3600
Hours (mean solar)	Seconds (sidereal)	3609.8565
Hours (mean solar)	Weeks (mean calendar)	0.0059523809
Hours (sidereal)	Days (mean solar)	0.41552899
Hours (sidereal)	Days (sidereal)	0.0416666
Hours (sidereal)	Hours (mean solar)	0.99726957
Hours (sidereal)	Minutes (mean solar)	59.836174
Hours (sidereal)	Minutes (sidereal)	60
Inches	Ångström units	2.54×10^8
Inches	Centimeters	2.54
Inches	Cubits	0.055555
Inches	Fathoms	0.013888
Inches	Feet	0.083333
Inches	Meters	0.0254

UNITS: CONVERSIONS AND CONSTANTS *(continued)*

FROM	TO	X BY
Inches	Mils	1000
Inches	Yards	0.027777
Kilograms	Drams(apoth. or troy)	257.20597
Kilograms	Drams (avdp.)	564.38339
Kilograms	Dynes	980665
Kilograms	Grains	15432.358
Kilograms	Hundredweights (long)	0.019684131
Kilograms	Hundredweights (short)	0.022046226
Kilograms	Ounces (apoth. or troy)	32.150737
Kilograms	Ounces (avdp.)	35.273962
Kilograms	Pennyweights	643.01493
Kilograms	Pounds (apoth. or troy)	2.6792289
Kilograms	Pounds (avdp.)	2.2046226
Kilograms	Quarters (U.S. long)	0.0039368261
Kilograms	Scruples (apoth.)	771.61792
Kilograms	Tons (long)	0.00098420653
Kilograms	Tons (metric)	0.001
Kilograms	Tons (short)	0.0011023113
Kilograms/cu. meter	Grams/cu. cm.	0.001
Kilograms/cu. meter	Lb. /cu. ft.	0.062427961
Kilograms/cu. meter	Lb./cu. inch	3.6127292×10^{-5}
Kiloliters	Cu. centimeters	1×10^{6}
Kiloliters	Cu. feet	35.31566
Kiloliters	Cu. inches	61025.45
Kiloliters	Cu. meters	1.000028
Kiloliters	Cu. yards	1.307987
Kiloliters	Gallons (U.S. dry)	27.0271
Kiloliters	Gallons (U.S. liq.)	264.1794
Kilometers	Astronomical units	6.68878×10^{-9}
Kilometers	Feet	3280.8399
Kilometers	Light years	1.05702×10^{-13}
Kilometers	Miles (naut. Int.)	0.53995680
Kilometers	Miles (statute)	0.62137119
Kilometers	Rods	198.83878
Kilometers	Yards	1093.6133
Kilometers/hr.	Cm./sec.	27.7777
Kilometers/hr.	Feet/hr.	3280.8399
Kilometers/hr.	Feet/min.	54.680665
Kilometers/hr.	Knots (Int.)	0.53995680
Kilometers/hr.	Meters/sec.	0.277777
Kilometers/hr.	Miles (statute)/hr.	0.62137119
Kilometers/min.	Cm./sec.	1666.666

UNITS: CONVERSIONS AND CONSTANTS (*continued*)

FROM	TO	X BY
Kilometers/min.	Feet/min.	3280.8399
Kilometers/min.	Kilometers/hr.	60
Kilometers/min.	Knots (Int.)	32.397408
Kilometers/min.	Miles/hr.	37.282272
Kilometers/min.	Miles/min.	0.62137119
Kilowatt-hours	Joules	3.6×10^6
Light, velocity of	299,792.4562 Km/sec. ± 1.1	meter/sec. (100x more accurate)
Light, velocity of	m/sec. ± 0.33ppm	$2.9979250(10) \times 10^8$
Light, velocity of	cm/sec. ± 0.33ppm	$2.9979250(10) \times 10^{10}$
Light years	Astronomical units	63279.5
Light years	Kilometers	9.46055×10^{12}
Light years	Miles (statute)	5.87851×10^{12}
Liters	Bushels (U.S.)	0.02837839
Liters	Cu. centimeters	1000
Liters	Cu. feet	0.03531566
Liters	Cu. inches	61.02545
Liters	Cu. meters	0.001
Liters	Cu. yards	0.001307987
Liters	Drams (U.S. fluid)	270.5198
Liters	Gallons (U.S. dry)	0.2270271
Liters	Gallons (U.S. liq.)	0.2641794
Liters	Gills (U.S.)	8.453742
Liters	Hogsheads	0.004193325
Liters	Minims (U.S.)	16231.19
Liters	Ounces (U.S. fluid)	33.81497
Liters	Pecks (U.S.)	0.1135136
Liters	Pints (U.S. dry)	1.816217
Liters	Pints (U.S. liq.)	2.113436
Liters	Quarts (U.S. dry)	0.9081084
Liters	Quarts (U.S. liq.)	1.056718
Liters/min	Cu. ft./min.	0.03531566
Liters/min	Cu. ft./sec.	0.0005885943
Liters/min	Gal. (U.S. liq.)/min.	0.2641794
Liters/sec.	Cu. ft./min.	2.118939
Liters/sec.	Cu. ft./sec.	0.03531566
Liters/sec.	Cu. yards/min.	0.07847923
Liters/sec.	Gal. (U.S. liq.)/min.	15.85077
Liters/sec.	Gal. (U.S. liq.)/sec.	0.2641794
Lumens	Candle power	0.079577472
Meters	Ångström units	1×10^{10}
Meters	Fathoms	0.54680665
Meters	Feet	3.2808399

UNITS: CONVERSIONS AND CONSTANTS *(continued)*

FROM	TO	X BY
Meters	Furlongs	0.0049709695
Meters	Inches	39.370079
Meters	Megameters	1×10^{-6}
Meters	Miles (naut. Int.)	0.00053995680
Meters	Miles (statute)	0.00062137119
Meters	Millimicrons	1×10^{9}
Meters	Mils	39370.079
Meters	Rods	0.19883878
Meters	Yards	1.0936133
Meters/hr.	Feet/hr.	3.2808399
Meters/hr.	Feet/min.	0.054680665
Meters/hr.	Knots (Int.)	0.00053995680
Meters/hr.	Miles (statute)/hr.	0.00062137119
Meters/min.	Cm./sec.	1.666666
Meters/min.	Feet/min.	3.2808399
Meters/min.	Feet/sec.	0.054680665
Meters/min.	Kilometers/hr.	0.06
Meters/min.	Knots (Int.)	0.032397408
Meters/min.	Miles (statute)/hr.	0.037282272
Meters/sec.	Feet/min.	196.85039
Meters/sec.	Feet/sec.	3.2808399
Meters/sec.	Kilometers/hr.	3.6
Meters/sec.	Kilometers/min.	0.06
Meters/sec.	Miles (statute)/hr.	2.2369363
Meter-candles	Lumens/sq. meter	1
Micrograms	Grams	1×10^{-6}
Micrograms	Milligrams	0.001
Micromicrons	Ångström units	0.01
Micromicrons	Centimeters	1×10^{-10}
Micromicrons	Inches	$3.9370079 \times 10^{-11}$
Micromicrons	Meters	1×10^{-12}
Micromicrons	Microns	1×10^{-6}
Microns	Ångström units	10000
Microns	Centimeters	0.0001
Microns	Feet	3.2808399×10^{-6}
Microns	Inches	3.9370070×10^{-5}
Microns	Meters	1×10^{-6}
Microns	Millimeters	0.001
Microns	Millimicrons	1000
Miles (statute)	Centimeters	160934.4
Miles (statute)	Feet	5280
Miles (statute)	Furlongs	8

UNITS: CONVERSIONS AND CONSTANTS *(continued)*

FROM	TO	X BY
Miles (statute)	Inches	63360
Miles (statute)	Kilometers	1.609344
Miles (statute)	Light years	1.70111×10^{-13}
Miles (statute)	Meters	1600.344
Miles (statute)	Miles (naut. Int.)	0.86897624
Miles (statute)	Myriameters	0.1609344
Miles (statute)	Rods	320
Miles (statute)	Yards	1760
Miles/hr.	Cm./sec.	44.704
Miles/hr.	Feet/hr.	5280
Miles/hr.	Feet/min.	88
Miles/hr.	Feet/sec	1.466666
Miles/hr.	Kilometers/hr.	1.609344
Miles/hr.	Knots (Int.)	0.86897624
Miles/hr.	Meters/min.	26.8224
Miles/hr.	Miles/min.	0.0166666
Miles/min.	Cm./sec.	2682.24
Miles/min.	Feet/hr.	316800
Miles/min.	Feet/sec.	88
Miles/min.	Kilometers/min.	1.609344
Miles/min.	Knots (Int.)	52.138574
Miles/min.	Meters/min.	1609.344
Miles/min.	Miles/hr.	60
Mlilligrams	Carats (1877)	0.004871
Mlilligrams	Carats (metric)	0.005
Milligrams	Drams (apoth. or troy)	0.00025720597
Mlilligrams	Drams (advp.)	0.00056438339
Milligrams	Grains	0.015432358
Milligrams	Grams	0.001
Milligrams	Ounces (apoth. or troy)	3.2150737×10^{-5}
Milligrams	Ounces (avdp.)	3.5273962×10^{-5}
Milligrams	Pounds (apoth. or troy)	2.6792289×10^{-5}
Milligrams	Pounds(avdp.)	2.2046226×10^{-6}
Milligrams/liter	Grains/gal. (U.S.)	0.05841620
Milligrams/liter	Grams/liter	0.001
Milligrams/liter	Parts/million	1; solvent density = 1
Milligrams/liter	Lb./cu. ft.	6.242621×10^{-5}
Milligrams/mm.	Dynes/cm.	9.80665
Milliliters	Cu. cm.	1
Milliliters	Cu. inches	0.06102545
Milliliters	Drams (U.S. fluid)	0.2705198
Milliliters	Gills (U.S.)	0.008453742

UNITS: CONVERSIONS AND CONSTANTS *(continued)*

FROM	TO	X BY
Milliliters	Minims (U.S.)	16.23119
Milliliters	Ounces (U.S. fluid)	0.03381497
Milliliters	Pints (U.S. liq.)	0.002113436
Millimeters	Ångatröm units	1×10^{7}
Millimeters	Centimeters	0.1
Millimeters	Decimeters	0.01
Millimeters	Dekameters	0.0001
Millimeters	Feet	0.0032808399
Millimeters	Inches	0.039370079
Millimeters	Meters	0.001
Millimeters	Microns	1000
Millimeters	Mils	39.370079
Millimicrons	Ångström units	10
Millimicrons	Centimeters	1×10^{-7}
Millimicrons	Inches	3.9370079×10^{-8}
Millimicrons	Microns	0.001
Millimicrons	Millimeters	1×10^{-6}
Minutes (angular)	Degrees	0.0166666
Minutes (angular)	Quadrants	0.000185185
Minutes (angular)	Radians	0.00029088821
Minutes (angular)	Seconds (angular)	60
Minutes (mean solar)	Days (mean solar)	0.0006944444
Minutes (mean solar)	Days (sidereal)	0.00069634577
Minutes (mean solar)	Hours (mean solar)	0.0166666
Minutes (mean solar)	Hours (sidereal)	0.016732298
Minutes (mean solar)	Minutes (sidereal)	1.00273791
Minutes (sidereal)	Days (mean solar)	0.00069254831
Minutes (sidereal)	Minutes (mean solar)	0.99726957
Minutes (sidereal)	Months (mean calendar)	2.2768712×10^{-5}
Minutes (sidereal)	Seconds (sidereal)	60
Minutes/cm.	Radians/cm.	0.00029088821
Months (lunar)	Days (mean solar)	29.530588
Months (lunar)	Hours (mean solar)	708.73411
Months (lunar)	Minutes (mean solar)	42524.047
Months (lunar)	Second (mean solar)	2.5514428×10^{-5}
Months (lunar)	Weeks (mean calendar)	4.2186554
Months (mean calendar)	Days (mean solar)	30.416666
Months (mean calendar)	Hours (mean solar) .	730
Months (mean calendar)	Months (lunar)	1.0300055
Months (mean calendar)	Weeks (mean calendar)	4.3452381
Months (mean calendar)	Years (calendar)	0.08333333
Months (mean calendar)	Years (sidereal)	0.083274845

UNITS: CONVERSIONS AND CONSTANTS *(continued)*

FROM	TO	X BY
Months (mean calendar)	Years (tropical)	0.083278075
Myriagrams	Pounds (avdp.)	22.046226
Ounces (avdp.)	Drams (apoth. or troy)	7.291666
Ounces (avdp.)	Drams (avdp.)	16
Ounces (avdp.)	Grains	437.5
Ounces (avdp.)	Grams	28.349
Ounces (avdp.)	Ounces (apoth. or troy)	0.9114583
Ounces (avdp.)	Pounds (apoth. or troy)	0.075954861
Ounces (avdp.)	Pounds(avdp.)	0.0625
Ounces (U.S. fluid)	Cu. cm.	29.573730
Ounces (U.S. fluid)	Cu.inches	1.8046875
Ounces (U.S. fluid)	Cu. meters	2.9573730×10^{-5}
Ounces (U.S. fluid)	Drams (U.S. fluid)	8
Ounces (U.S. fluid)	Gallons (U.S. dry)	0.0067138047
Ounces (U.S. fluid)	Gallons (U.S. liq.)	0.0078125
Ounces (U.S. fluid)	Gills (U.S.)	0.25
Ounces (U.S. fluid)	Liters	0.029572702
Ounces (U.S. fluid)	Pints (U.S. liq.)	0.0625
Ounces (U.S. fluid)	Quarts (U.S. liq.)	0.03125
Ounces/sq. inch	Dynes/sq. cm.	4309.22
Ounces/sq. inch	Grams/sq. cm.	4.3941849
Ounces/sq. inch	Pounds/sq. ft.	9
Ounces/sq. inch	Pounds/sq. inch	0.0625
Parts/million	Grains/gal. (U.S.)	0.05841620
Parts/million	Grams/liter	0.001
Parts/million	Milligrams/Liter	1
Pints (U.S. dry)	Bushels (U.S.)	0.015625
Pints (U.S. dry)	Cu. cm.	550.61047
Pints (U.S. dry)	Cu. inches	33.6003125
Pints (U.S. dry)	Gallons (U.S. dry)	0.125
Pints (U.S. dry)	Gallons (U.S. liq.)	0.14545590
Pints (U.S. dry)	Liters	0.5505951
Pints (U.S. dry)	Pecks (U.S.)	0.0625
Pints (U.S. dry)	Quarts (U.S. dry)	0.5
Pints (U.S. liq.)	Cu. cm.	473.17647
Pints (U.S. liq.)	Cu. feet	0.016710069
Pints (U.S. liq.)	Cu. inches	28.875
Pints (U.S. liq.)	Cu. yards	0.00061889146
Pints (U.S. liq.)	Drama (U.S. fluid)	128
Pints (U.S. liq.)	Gallons (U.S. liq.)	0.125
Pints (U.S. liq.)	Gills (U.S.)	4
Pints (U.S. liq.)	Liters	0.4731632

UNITS: CONVERSIONS AND CONSTANTS *(continued)*

FROM	TO	X BY
Pints (U.S. liq.)	Milliliters	473.1632
Pints (U.S. liq.)	Minims (U.S.)	7680
Pints (U.S. liq.)	Ounces (U.S. fluid)	16
Pints (U.S. liq.)	Quarts (U.S. liq.)	0.5
Planck's constant	Erg-seconds	6.6255×10^{-27}
Planck's constant	Joule-seconds	6.6255×10^{-34}
Planck's constant	Joule-sec./Avog. No. (chem.)	3.9905×10^{-10}
Pounds (apoth. or troy)	Drams (apoth. or troy)	96
Pounds (apoth. or troy)	Drams (avdp.)	210.65143
Pounds (apoth. or troy)	Grains	5780
Pounds (apoth. or troy)	Grams	373.24172
Pounds (apoth. or troy)	Kilograms	0.37324172
Pounds (apoth. or troy)	Ounces (apoth. or troy)	12
Pounds (apoth. or troy)	Ounces (avdp.)	13.165714
Pounds (apoth. or troy)	Pounds(avdp.)	0.8228571
Pounds (avdp.)	Drams (apoth. or troy)	116.6686
Pounds (avdp.)	Drams (avdp.)	256
Pounds (avdp.)	Grains	7000
Pounds (avdp.)	Grams	453.59237
Pounds (avdp.)	Kilograms	0.45359237
Pounds (avdp.)	Ounces (apoth. or troy)	14.593333
Pounds (avdp.)	Ounces (avdp.)	16
Pounds (avdp.)	Pounds (apoth. or troy)	1.215277
Pounds (avdp.)	Scruples (apoth.)	350
Pounds (avdp.)	Tons (long)	0.00044642857
Pounds (avdp.)	Tons (metric)	0.00045359237
Pounds (avdp.)	Tons (short)	0.0005
Pounds/cu.ft.	Grams/cu. cm.	0.016018463
Pounds/cu.ft.	Kg./cu. meter	16.018463
Pounds/cu. inch	Grams/cu. cm.	27.679905
Pounds/cu. inch	Grams/liter	27.68068
Pounds/cu. inch	Kg./cu. meter	27679.005
Pounds/gal.(U. S.liq.)	Grams/cu. cm.	0.11982643
Pounds/gal.(U. S.liq.)	Pounds/cu. ft.	7.4805195
Pounds/inch	Grams/cm	178.57967
Pounds/inch	Grams/ft.	5443.1084
Pounds/inch	Grams/inch	453.59237
Pounds/inch	Ounces/cm.	6.2992
Pounds/inch	Ounces/inch	16
Pounds/inch	Pounds/meter	39.370079
Pounds/minute	Kilograms/hr.	27.2155422
Pounds/minute	Kilograms/min.	0.45359237

UNITS: CONVERSIONS AND CONSTANTS *(continued)*

FROM	TO	X BY
Pounds on Earth =1	Pounds on Mars	0.3627 Equatorial
Pounds on Earth =1	Pounds on Mercury	0.3648 Equatorial
Pounds on Earth =1	Pounds on Moon	0.1652 Equatorial
Pounds on Earth =1	Pounds on Neptune	1.323 ± 0.210 Equatorial
Pounds on Earth =1	Pounds on Pluto	0.0225 ± 0.217 Equatorial
Pounds on Earth =1	Pounds on Saturn	0.8800 Equatorial
Pounds on Earth =1	Pounds on Sun	27.905 Equatorial
Pounds on Earth =1	Pounds on Uranus	0.9554 ± 0.168 Equatorial
Pounds on Earth =1	Pounds on Venus	0.9049 Equatorial
Pounds/sq. ft.	Atmospheres	0.000472541
Pounds/sq. ft.	Bars	0.000478803
Pounds/sq. ft.	Cm. of Hg (0°C.)	0.0359131
Pounds/sq. ft.	Dynes/sq. cm.	478.803
Pounds/sq. ft.	Ft. of air (1 atm. 60°F.)	13.096
Pounds/sq. ft.	Grams/sq. cm.	0.48824276
Pounds/sq. ft.	Kg./sq. meter	4.8824276
Pounds/sq. ft.	Mm. of Hg (0°C.)	0.369131
Pounds/sq. inch	Atmospheres	0.0680460
Pounds/sq. inch	Bars	0.0689476
Pounds/sq. inch	Dynes/sq. cm.	68947.6
Pounds/sq. inch	Grams/sq. cm.	70.306958
Pounds/sq. inch	Kg./sq. cm.	0.070306958
Pounds/sq. inch	Mm. of Hg (0°C.)	51.7149
Quarts (U.S. dry)	Bushels (U.S.)	0.03125
Quarts (U.S. dry)	Cu. cm.	1101.2209
Quarts (U.S. dry)	Cu. feet	0.038889251
Quarts (U.S. dry	Cu. inches	67.200625
Quarts (U.S. dry)	Gallons (U.S. dry)	0.25
Quarts (U.S. dry)	Gallons (U.S. liq.)	0.29091180
Quarts (U.S. dry)	Liters	1.1011901
Quarts (U.S. dry)	Pecks (U.S.)	0.125
Quarts (U.S. dry)	Pints (U.S. dry)	2
Quarts (U.S. liq.)	Cu. cm.	946.35295
Quarts (U.S. liq.)	Cu. feet	0.033420136
Quarts (U.S. liq.)	Cu. inches	57.75
Quarts (U.S. liq.)	Drams (U.S. fluid)	256
Quarts (U.S. liq.)	Gallons (U.S. dry)	0.21484175
Quarts (U.S. liq.)	Gallons (U.S. liq.)	0.25
Quarts (U.S. liq.)	Gills (U.S.)	8
Quarts (U.S. liq.)	Liters	0.9463264

UNITS: CONVERSIONS AND CONSTANTS *(continued)*

FROM	TO	X BY
Quarts (U.S. liq.)	Ounces (U.S. fluid)	32
Quarts (U.S. liq.)	Pints (U.S. liq.)	2
Quarts (U.S. liq.)	Quarts (U.S. dry)	0.8593670
Quintals (metric)	Grams	100000
Quintals (metric)	Hundredweights (long)	1.9684131
Quintals (metric)	Kilograms	100
Quintals (metric)	Pounds (avdp.)	220.46226
Radians	Circumferences	0.15915494
Radians	Degrees	57.295779
Radians	Minutes	3437.7468
Radians	Quadrants	0.63661977
Radians	Revolutions	0.15915494
Revolutions	Degrees	360
Revolutions	Grades	400
Revolutions	Quadrants	4
Revolutions	Radians	6.2831853
Seconds (angular)	Degrees	0.000277777
Seconds (angular)	Minutes	0.0166666
Seconds (angular)	Radians	4.8481368×10^{-6}
Seconds (mean solar)	Days (mean solar)	1.1574074×10^{-5}
Seconds (mean solar)	Days (sidereal)	1.1605763×10^{-5}
Seconds (mean solar)	Hours (mean solar)	0.0002777777
Seconds (mean solar)	Hours (sidereal)	0.00027853831
Seconds (mean solar)	Minutes (mean solar)	0.0166666
Seconds (mean solar)	Minutes (sidereal)	0.016712298
Seconds (mean solar)	Seconds (sidereal)	1.00273791
Seconds (sidereal)	Days (mean solar)	1.1542472×10^{-5}
Seconds (sidereal)	Days (sidereal)	1.1574074×10^{-5}
Seconds (sidereal)	Hours (mean solar)	0.00027701932
Seconds (sidereal)	Hours (sidereal)	0.000277777
Seconds (sidereal)	Minutes (mean solar)	0.016621159
Seconds (sidereal)	Minutes (sidereal)	0.0166666
Seconds (sidereal)	Seconds (mean solar)	0.09726957
Sq. Centimeters	Sq. decimeters	0.01
Sq. centimeters	Sq. feet	0.0010763910
Sq. Centimeters	Sq. inches	0.15500031
Sq. Centimeters	Sq. meters	0.0001
Sq. centimeters	Sq. mm.	100
Sq. centimeters	Sq. mile	155000.31
Sq. centimeters	Sq. yards	0.00011959900
Sq. decimeters	Sq. cm.	100
Sq. Decimeters	Sq. inches	15.500031

UNITS: CONVERSIONS AND CONSTANTS *(continued)*

FROM	TO	X BY
Sq. dekameters	Acres	0.024710538
Sq. dekameters	Ares	1
Sq. dekameters	Sq. meters	100
Sq. dekameters	Sq. yards	119.59900
Sq. feet	Acres	2.295684×10^{-5}
Sq. feet	Ares	0.0009290304
Sq. feet	Sq. cm.	929.0304
Sq. feet	Sq.inches	144
Sq. feet	Sq. meters	0.09290304
Sq. feet	Sq. miles	3.5870064×10^{-8}
Sq. Feet	Sq. yards	0.111111
Sq. Hectometers	Sq. meters	10000
Sq. inches	Sq. cm.	6.4516
Sq. inches	Sq. decimeters	0.064516
Sq. inches	Sq. feet	0.0069444
Sq. inches	Sq. meters	0.00064516
Sq. inches	Sq. miles	$2.4909767 \times 10^{-10}$
Sq. inches	Sq. mm	645.16
Sq. inches	Sq. mils	1×10^{-6}
Sq. kilometers	Acres	247.10538
Sq. Kilometers	Sq. feet	1.0763010×10^{7}
Sq. Kilometers	Sq. inches	1.5500031×10^{9}
Sq. Kilometers	Sq. meters	1×10^{6}
Sq. Kilometers	Sq. miles	0.38610216
Sq. Kilometers	Sq. yards	1.1959900×10^{6}
Sq. meters	Acres	0.00024710538
Sq. meters	Ares	0.01
Sq. meters	Hectares	0.0001
Sq. meters	Sq. cm	10000
Sq. meters	Sq. feet	10.763910
Sq. meters	Sq. inches	1550.0031
Sq. meters	Sq. kilometers	1×10^{-6}
Sq. meters	Sq. miles	3.8610218×10^{-7}
Sq. meters	Sq. mm	1×10^{6}
Sq. meters	Sq. yards	1.1959900
Sq. miles	Acres	640
Sq. miles	Hectares	258.99881
Sq. miles	Sq. feet	2.7878288×10^{7}
Sq. miles	Sq. kilometers	2.5899881
Sq. miles	Sq. meters	2589988.1
Sq. miles	Sq. rods	102400
Sq. miles	Sq. yards	3.0976×10^{6}

UNITS: CONVERSIONS AND CONSTANTS *(continued)*

FROM	TO	X BY
Sq. millimeters	Sq. cm.	0.01
Sq. millimeters	Sq.inches	0.0015500031
Sq. millimeters	Sq. meters	1×10^{-6}
Sq. yards	Acres	0.00020661157
Sq. yards	Ares	0.0083612736
Sq. yards	Hectares	8.3612736×10^{-5}
Sq. yards	Sq. cm	8361.2736
Sq. yards	Sq. feet	9
Sq. yards	Sq. inches	1296
Sq. yards	Sq. meters	0.83612736
Sq. yards	Sq. miles	$3.228305785 \times 10^{-7}$
Tons (long)	Kilograms	1016.0469
Tons (long)	Ounces (avdp.)	35840
Tons (long)	Pounds (apoth. or troy)	2722.22
Tons (long)	Pounds(avdp.)	2240
Tons (long)	Tons (metric)	1.0160469
Tons (long)	Tons (short)	1.12
Tons (metric)	Dynes	9.80665×10^{8}
Tons (metric)	Grams	1×10^{6}
Tons (metric)	Kilograms	1000
Tons (metric)	Ounces (avdp.)	35273.962
Tons (metric)	Pounds (apoth. or troy)	2679.2289
Tons (metric)	Pounde(avdp.)	2204.6226
Tons (metric)	Tons (long)	0.98420653
Tons (metric)	Tons (short)	1.1023113
Tons (short)	Kilograms	907.18474
Tons (short)	Ounces (avdp.)	32000
Tons (short)	Pounds (apoth. or troy)	2430.555
Tons (short)	Pounds(avdp.)	2000
Tons (short)	Tons (long)	0.89285714
Tons (short)	Tons (metric)	0.90718474
Velocity of light	cm/sec. ± 0.33ppm	$2.9979250(10) \times 10^{10}$
Velocity of light	m/sec. ± 0.33ppm	$2.9979250(10) \times 10^{8}$
Velocity of light (100xmore accurate)	Km/sec. ± 1.1 meter/sec.	$2.997924562 \times 10^{5}$
Volts	Mks. (r or nr) units	1
Volts (Int.)	Volts	1.000330
Volt-seconds	Maxwells	1×10^{8}
Watts	Kilowatts	0.001
Watts (Int.)	Watts	1.000165
Weeks (mean calendar)	Days (mean solar)	7
Weeks (mean calendar)	Days (sidereal)	7.0191654
Weeks (mean calendar)	Hours (mean solar)	168

UNITS: CONVERSIONS AND CONSTANTS *(continued)*

FROM	TO	X BY
Weeks (mean calendar)	Hours (sidereal)	168.45997
Weeks (mean calendar)	Minutes (mean solar)	10080
Weeks (mean calendar)	Minutes (sidereal)	10107.598
Weeks (mean calendar)	Months (lunar)	0.23704235
Weeks (mean calendar)	Months (mean calendar)	0.23013699
Weeks (mean calendar)	Years (calendar)	0.019178082
Weeks (mean calendar)	Years (sidereal)	0.019164622
Weeks (mean calendar)	Years (tropical)	0.019165365
Yards	Centimeters	91.44
Yards	Cubits	2
Yards	Fathoms	0.5
Yards	Feet.	3
Yards	Furlongs	0.00454545
Yards	Inches	36
Yards	Meters	0.9144
Yards	Rods	0.181818
Yards	Spans	4
Years (calendar)	Days (mean solar)	365
Years (calendar)	Hours (mean solar)	8760
Years (calendar)	Minutes (mean solar)	525600
Years (calendar)	Months (lunar)	12.360065
Years (calendar)	Months (mean calendar)	12
Years (calendar)	Seconds (mean solar)	3.1536×10^7
Years (calendar)	Weeks (mean calendar)	52.142857
Years (calendar)	Years (sidereal)	0.99929814
Years (calendar)	Years (tropical)	0.99933690
Years (leap)	Days (mean solar)	366
Years (sidereal)	Days (mean solar)	365.25636
Years (sidereal)	Days (sidereal)	366.25640
Years (sidereal)	Years (calendar)	1.0007024
Years (sidereal)	Years (tropical)	1.0000388
Years (tropical)	Days (mean solar)	365.24219
Years (tropical)	Days (sidereal)	366.24219
Years (tropical)	Hours (mean solar)	8765.8126
Years (tropical)	Hours (sidereal)	8789.8126
Years (tropical)	Months (mean calendar)	12.007963
Years (tropical)	Seconds (mean solar)	3.1556926×10^7
Years (tropical)	Seconds (sidereal)	3.1643326×10^7
Years (tropical)	Weeks (mean calendar)	52.177456
Years (tropical)	Years (Calendar)	1.0006635
Years (tropical)	Years (sidereal)	0.99996121

CHART OF ELEMENTS

Atomic#	Name	Symbol	Atomic Mass	Electrons K,L,M,N,O,P,Q	Atomic #	Name	Symbol	Atomic Mass	Electrons K,L,M,N,O,P,Q
1	Hydrogen	H	1.0079	1	53	Iodine	I	126.9045	2,8,18,18,7
2	Helium	He	4.00260	2	54	Xenon	Xe	131.30	2,8,18,18,8
3	Lithium	Li	6.941	2,1	55	Cesium	Cs	132.9054	2,8,18,18,8,1
4	Beryllium	Be	9.01218	2,2	56	Barium	Ba	137.34	2,8,18,18,8,2
5	Boron	B	10.81	2,3	57	Lanthanum	La	138.9055	2,8,18,18,9,2
6	Carbon	C	12.011	2,4	58	Cerium	Ce	140.12	2,8,18,20,8,2
7	Nitrogen	N	14.0067	2,5	59	Praseodymium	Pr	140.9077	2,8,18,21,8,2
8	Oxygen	O	15.9994	2,6	60	Neodymium	Nd	144.24	2,8,18,22,8,2
9	Fluorine	F	18.99840	2,7	61	Promethium	Pm	(145)	2,8,18,23,8,2
10	Neon	Ne	20.179	2,8	62	Samarium	Sm	150.4	2,8,18,24,8,2
11	Sodium	Na	22.98977	2,8,1	63	Europium	Eu	151.96	2,8,18,25,8,2
12	Magnesium	Mg	24.305	2,8,2	64	Gadolinium	Gd	157.25	2,8,18,25,9,2
13	Aluminum	Al	26.98154	2,8,3	65	Terbium	Tb	158.9254	2,8,18,27,8,2
14	Silicon	Si	28.086	2,8,4	66	Dysprosium	Dy	162.50	2,8,18,28,8,2
15	Phosphorus	P	30.97376	2,8,5	67	Holmium	Ho	164.9304	2,8,18,29,8,2
16	Sulfur	S	32.06	2,8,6	68	Erbium	Er	167.26	2,8,18,30,8,2
17	Chlorine	Cl	35.453	2,8,7	69	Thulium	Tm	168.9342	2,8,18,31,8,2
18	Argon	Ar	39.948	2,8,8	70	Ytterbium	Yb	173.04	2,8,18,32,8,2
19	Potassium	K	39.098	2,8,8,1	71	Lutetium	Lu	174.97	2,8,18,32,9,2
20	Calcium	Ca	40.08	2,8,8,2	72	Hafnium	Hf	178.49	2,8,18,32,10,2
21	Scandium	Sc	44.9559	2,8,9,2	73	Tantalum	Ta	180.9479	2,8,18,32,11,2
22	Titanium	Ti	47.90	2,8,10,2	74	Tungsten	W	183.85	2,8,18,32,12,3
23	Vanadium	V	50.9414	2,8,11,2	75	Rhenium	Re	186.207	2,8,18,32,13,2
24	Chromium	Cr	51.996	2,8,13,1	76	Osmium	Os	190.2	2,8,18,32,14,2
25	Manganese	Mn	54.9380	2,8,13,2	77	Iridium	Ir	192.22	2,8,18,32,15,2
26	Iron	Fe	55.847	2,8,14,2	78	Platinum	Pt	195.09	2,8,18,32,17,1
27	Cobalt	Co	58.9332	2,8,15,2	79	Gold	Au	196.9665	2,8,18,32,18,1
28	Nickel	Ni	58.70	2,8,16,2	80	Mercury	Hg	200.59	2,8,18,32,18,2
29	Copper	Cu	63.546	2,8,18,1	81	Thallium	Tl	204.37	2,8,18,32,18,3
30	Zinc	Zn	65.37	2,8,18,2	82	Lead	Pb	207.2	2,8,18,32,18,4
31	Gallium	Ga	69.72	2,8,18,3	83	Bismuth	Bi	208.9804	2,8,18,32,18,5
32	Germanium	Ge	72.59	2,8,18,4	84	Polonium	Po	(209)	2,8,18,32,18,6
33	Arsenic	As	74.9216	2,8,18,5	85	Astatine	At	(210)	2,8,18,32,18,7
34	Selenium	Se	78.96	2,8,18,6	86	Radon	Rn	(222)	2,8,18,32,18,8
35	Bromine	Br	79.904	2,8,18,7	87	Francium	Fr	(223)	2,8,18,32,18,8,1
36	Krypton	Kr	83.80	2,8,18,8	88	Radium	Ra	226.0254	2,8,18,32,18,8,2
37	Rubidium	Rb	101.07	2,8,18,15,1	89	Actinium	Ac	(227)	2,8,18,32,18,9,2
38	Strontium	Sr	87.63	2,8,18,8,2	90	Thorium	Th	232.0381	2,8,18,32,18,10,2
39	Yttrium	Y	88.92	2,8,18,9,2	91	Protactinium	Pa	231.0359	2,8,18,32,20,9,2
40	Zirconium	Zr	91.22	2,8,18,10,2	92	Uranium	U	238.029	2,8,18,32,21,9,2
41	Niobium	Nb	92.91	2,8,18,12,1	93	Neptunium	Np	237.0482	2,8,18,32,22,9,2
42	Molybdenum	Mo	95.95	2,8,18,13,1	94	Plutonium	Pu	(244)	2,8,18,32,24,8,2
43	Technetium	Tc	(99)	2,8,18,14,1	95	Americium	Am	(243)	2,8,18,32,25,8,2
44	Ruthenium	Ru	101.7	2,8,18,15,1	96	Curium	Cm	(247)	2,8,18,32,25,9,2
45	Rhodium	Rh	102.9055	2,8,18,16,1	98	Californium	Cf	(251)	2,8,18,32,28,8,2
46	Palladium	Pd	106.4	2,8,18,18,0	99	Einsteinium	Es	(254)	2,8,18,32,29,8,2
47	Silver	Ag	107.868	2,8,18,18,1	100	Fermium	m	(257)	2,8,18,32,30,8,2
49	Indium	In	114.82	2,8,18,18,3	101	Mendelevium	Md	(258)	2,8,18,32,31,8,2
50	Tin	Sn	118.69	2,8,18,18,4	102	Nobelium	No	(255)	2,8,18,32,32,8,2
51	Antimony	Sb	121.75	2,8,18,18,5	103	Lawrencium	Lr	(260)	2,8,18,32,32,9,2
52	Tellurium	Te	127.60	2,8,18,18,6					

Index